A Farming Century

William G. G. Alexander.

A Farming Century
The Darent Valley
1892–1992

WILLIAM G. G. ALEXANDER

QUILLER PRESS
LONDON

This book is to the
memory of Marion

Beloved
Wife
Mother
Grandmother

First published 1991 by Quiller Press Limited
46 Lillie Road
London SW6 1TN

© William G. G. Alexander 1991

ISBN 1 870948 53 X

Printed in Great Britain by St Edmundsbury Press
Typeset by Goodfellow & Egan Ltd, Cambridge
Produced by Hugh Tempest-Radford *Book Producers*

Contents

Acknowledgements

My first thanks are to Barbara Laming whose advice and encouragement gave me confidence to write this book. Secondly, I have received invaluable help from my brother James in providing information and especially for many of the photographs from his own vast collection.

My research took me to many places about which I had heard but had not seen. This gave me much pleasure in talking to friends and relations, both old and new. I thank them very much for all their information.

The three family trees were produced from searching information provided by the Allan family, the Greenlees family, the Steven family and the Alexander families to all of whom I am much indebted.

The research carried out in Scotland was greatly helped with information provided by John and Helen Reid, Elizabeth Anderson and R.L. Johnston. Dr. C.C. Lee provided information and two photographs from Lochwinnoch Community Museum (Department of Arts and Libraries, Renfrew District Council). My thanks are also coupled with the assistance given by the librarians and the research facilities in Paisley, Glasgow and Edinburgh.

Local libraries in Dartford, Sevenoaks, Swanley, Tunbridge Wells and Maidstone provided useful local information, much of it being stored on microfilm.

Personal recollections and photographs deserve my very special thanks. These are to my sister Mary, to Betty Brown, Ben Brice, Ethel Darby, Keith Denham, Neville Free, Guy Hart-Dyke, John Hever, Paul Lambert, Dolly Mills (née Gaston), Reg Morgan, Leslie Strickland, Jimmy and Violet Turnball, Eric Watts, the Topham Photo Library, the Royal Victoria and Bull Hotel and a very special thank you to the family of Joseph Larter who had retained his personal diary which recorded the date on which the Alexander family moved into Home Farm house.

Technical information was compiled with assistance from Brian Akers, Gordon Ancorn, Mike Bax, Bob Boon, Nigel Britten, Alfie Marr, Geoff Nutkins and Richard Prall. My thanks go to them all.

I am grateful to the following for allowing the use of information and photographs from their publications, St Martins Church, Eynsford, Cameron Books "War in the Countryside", Meresborough Books "Byegone Kent", John Murray "Harry Ferguson", National Farmers Union, Jenny Pearce "Location map" and sketches. Susan Pitman "Lullingstone Estate", Shire Publication "Dairying Byegones", Shuter and Shooter (Pty) Ltd "Chance Encounters" and The Holstein Friesian Cattle Society.

Anthony Rosen, whom I have known for over thirty years, has been a guiding star through the intricacies of publishing and I am very grateful to him for this as well as his contribution of the Preface. David Mynett's painting and illustrations have added considerable artistic eloquence, especially the eye catching painting of the book jacket. Jeremy Greenwood of Quiller Press Limited has been most enthusiastic in blending the photographs with my manuscript and I have appreciated his expertise. Douglas and Margaret Keen deserve a special mention for their meticulous proof-reading.

Lastly, but not least by any means, I am very aware of the tremendous patience which my wife Diana had in reading the draft chapters and in tolerating many solitary hours whilst I was writing. The composite illustration on the back of the jacket painted by her, required much thought and imagination. Thank you Diana for all your contributions. I hope that you will have as much pleasure in the reading as I have had in the research and writing of "A Farming Century in the Darent Valley".

Preface

by Anthony Rosen

The history of British farming is in danger of being lost to future generations because so many of those who have helped to shape the current pattern in our rural areas are failing to record their memories.

Nobody can accuse William Alexander of failing in this respect. His book *A Farming Century: The Darent Valley, 1892–1992* gives the reader a frank and personal insight into the building of the Alexander Empire—for indeed this is what it is.

William, now in his sixties (and with five grandchildren of his own), traces the family back to when his grandfather, James Alexander, a tenant farmer in Scotland, moved south to take over the tenancy of Home Farm, Eynsford, Kent, in 1891. The love and respect which William, his brother James, and their father and grandfather before them—and now their sons—have for their land shines through the book. This is especially interesting at a time when farming is undergoing its greatest economic crisis for over fifty years.

It is a very personal story told with sensitivity by a countryman who has earned the respect of his peers by the innovative leadership he has displayed during his own half a century of practical farming. Those who know William will be impressed by his honesty and will find this book a fascinating glimpse behind the always cheerful and humorous presence of a true gentleman. And for those who wonder how the British countryside has achieved its present glory this book will provide many of the answers.

Of the Alexanders themselves no words could be more pertinent than 'A farmer should farm as though he is going to live for ever, but live as though he is going to die tomorrow.'

This book will make an impressive contribution to Britain's farming library. I am proud to be associated with it.

The Darent Valley

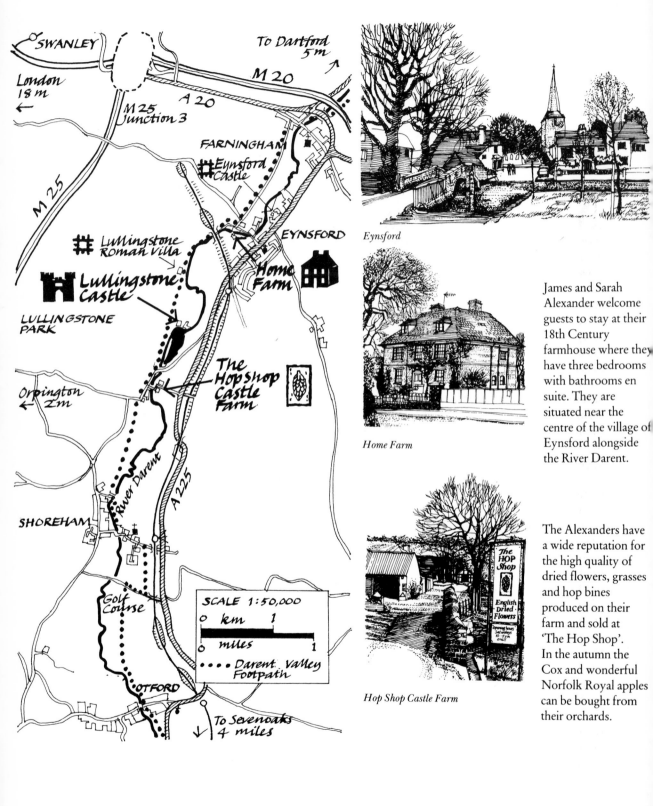

Eynsford

Home Farm

Hop Shop Castle Farm

James and Sarah Alexander welcome guests to stay at their 18th Century farmhouse where they have three bedrooms with bathrooms en suite. They are situated near the centre of the village of Eynsford alongside the River Darent.

The Alexanders have a wide reputation for the high quality of dried flowers, grasses and hop bines produced on their farm and sold at 'The Hop Shop'. In the autumn the Cox and wonderful Norfolk Royal apples can be bought from their orchards.

CHAPTER 1
The Alexander Family

My grandfather, James Alexander, took over the tenancy of Home Farm, Eynsford, in Kent on 29 September 1891, though he and his family did not occupy the farmhouse until 4 February 1892. The farm consisted of 102 acres of land, a big farmhouse and two farm cottages. There was a very large old Kent Barn with a thickly thatched roof, stables with hay lofts and other ancillary buildings.

David Greenlees, my grandmother's brother, had been farming at Broughton Farm, Otford, at the foot of the North Downs, near Sevenoaks in Kent, for several years and the two families had always kept in close touch with each other. The Greenlees' prosperity was envied by my grandparents, and now, aged fifty-seven and forty-four, with a family of four children aged eight to fifteen, they felt that it was time to consider a move south, soon or never. David Greenlees was therefore asked to keep his ears and eyes open for any farms, suitable for dairying, to rent in the area. When Home Farm, Eynsford, came onto the market, my grandfather went to see it at once and inspected the land, the farmhouse and the buildings. The location and size of the farm were ideal, and the river Darent, a flourishing trout stream, running through the meadows gave an added attraction, as well as Eynsford railway station being close by. Scotsmen are considered to be very canny in making up their minds. This opportunity required prompt action and I understand that it was my grandmother who eventually tipped the scales in favour of moving. There was the added benefit of being only four miles away from her brother at Otford.

In Scotland my grandparents were tenants of a farm at Lochwinnoch, Renfrewshire, sixteen miles south-west of Glasgow. It was called East Auchengown and was first rented by my great-grandparents in 1863. Although in my youth, when motoring from Beith to Paisley, I had looked many times across the hills from Lochwinnoch to Auchengown and was told that the 'wee hoose' up there was where my father came from, I was never actually taken there. I did not realize at the time what an interesting wealth of history would have awaited me. In the preparation for writing this book, my very first visit therefore was in the summer of 1986, following a letter I had written to the occupier. I had not realized there were three farms within a few yards of each other, called East, Mid, and West Auchengown. I received a very warm welcome at each one, finding that, in true Scottish tradition, by the time I arrived the bush telegraph had been busy. Each one had found out almost more about me than I knew myself, particularly of the family tree.

East Auchengown was the farm that I really was seeking, and John and Helen Reid, the owners and farmers, gave me a great deal of help. Helen produced two cardboard boxes of dust-covered documents from somewhere in the attic and kindly allowed me to wade through them in search of information about my grandparents.

My great-grandparents, William and Martha Alexander took the tenancy of the

James Alexander (third from left) and Jane Alexander, née Greenlees (third from left) with other members of the Greenlees family.

sixty-five acres in 1863 at an annual rent of £81. The farmhouse, like the byre, which had standings for thirteen cows, was built with local quarried stone and had slate-covered roofs. The byre joined on to the 'milk hoose' which in turn led through to the farmhouse kitchen. You could, in theory at least (and in practice when the wife wasn't looking!) go from the kitchen through to the byre to have a last look at the cows before going to bed. The cows and young stock were the life-line of the farm and, quite rightly, received every attention.

The farm was all grass, the fields small and on a hilly land. Two-thirds lay along the upper edge of a narrow country lane, which at the time was the main road, and the other third, the lower edge. Being right by the roadside was convenient for taking the milk in the buggy cart down to Lochwinnoch Station, from where it went to the dairies at Paisley and Glasgow. The water supply was from a loch a mile or so away up in the hills, and lighting was of course by paraffin lamps. Coal for fires and heating water was readily available from the coal mines in the district.

Although the grass for hay was cut with horses and a mower, much of it was turned by hand to help it to 'make' so this was a time of year for 'all hands on deck'. Large hayricks on a wood log base were built in the stack-yard close to the farm buildings. They were thatched with reeds cut from the wetlands in the locality, and hay ropes, weighted down with iron or stones, helped to keep the thatch in place against the strong winds that blew in the winter. The stack-yard was a grand place for the free (in fact very free) range hens to scratch about and make little dust bowls and to lay their eggs in out-of-the-way places: under the hedgerows, in a discarded implement overgrown with grass and weeds, wherever they were out of sight and undisturbed. In the spring it was not uncommon to see a hatching of chicks appearing from a stack bottom where there had been space between the logs for the hen to lay her eggs and hatch them.

East Auchengown farm 1990.

A farmer's wife worked every bit as hard as the farmer himself, milking cows, feeding the calves, washing the dairy dishes and doing outside work at the busy time. Feeding calves was a skill that was particularly possessed by women. They had the motherly instinct of being able to tell when a calf was likely to be 'no' weel' and to remedy this much earlier than men would. As the farmer's family grew up all were automatically involved in helping either on the farm or in the house, and often both. The families were usually large, and, as small farms could not support two families, it is no wonder that there was such a demand for farms when the children were ready to leave home that they often had to go far afield.

Lochwinnoch is the second largest parish in Renfrewshire and neighbours the County of Ayrshire to its south, while Glasgow is on its north-east border. The population in 1791 was 2,613. At that time the textile industry was as important as the farming industry. The records for 1791 show that there were:

148 Farmers	2 Grocers
380 Cotton-mill workers	2 Butchers
135 Weavers	2 Surgeons
19 Tailors	1 Lawyer
14 Shoemakers	2 Schoolmasters
31 Smiths (blacksmiths, etc)	14 Ale sellers
39 Wrights (wheelwrights, etc)	1 Kirk Minister
17 Masons	

There was a very large loch and some strong-flowing rivers from the hills. All these turned huge water-wheels which were up to 24 feet in diameter and 10 feet wide. They were able to generate sufficient power to turn the machinery in the textile mills.

Before the 1700s spinning went on in most houses. It was in fact a daily occupation

The byre 1986.

of the women, who spun and dyed the wool from their own sheep. This was in turn woven by their husbands. The cloth was made up by the village tailor into clothes for men and women. In the early 1700s linen and cambric manufacture was introduced into Paisley and farmers were encouraged to grow flax. All the fine linen made in Scotland was at one time sent to Holland to be bleached. However, grants were later given by the Board of Manufacturers to the Scottish people to encourage them to establish bleach fields and this created much activity in Lochwinnoch. One company, it was said, used all the buttermilk from the making of cheese for the bleaching process; this continued until about 1756 when Dr Home of Edinburgh taught them to use sulphuric acid in its place. One of the bleach fields that was established was at Loanhead—a farm later owned by my uncle and where I stayed with my cousins during my school holidays in the summer.

Threadmaking was introduced in the early 1720s, and at its height the industry had twenty thread mills in the parish. This trade lasted over a hundred years. Handloom weaving was carried out quite extensively in the cottages until the end of the nineteenth century. A major product was the beautiful Pine Pattern shawls woven in silk, cotton and wool. Much of this work survives today in christening robes. The textiles industry created a great stimulus in Lochwinnoch and the 1791 population of 2,613 increased to 4,515 by 1831.

Auchengown farm was run by family labour as were most of the other farms in the district, but larger farms needed to hire servants. The method of engaging help in Scotland was entirely different from that in England. Servants were hired by half-year or yearly arrangements, the terms being from 28th November and 28th May. The dates suited the farming operations as by the 1st November all the 'tatties' were harvested and safely stored, the turnip shawing was well forward, and cows and calves were housed for the winter. It was necessary for the farmer to know if his worker was continuing for a further period or if he would need to engage another man; 'Speirin' (asking) time was at the beginning of the month and it was naturally an anxious time for the workers as well as the farmer. If the boss had not 'speired' you to stay on for another term, then you would have to look for another job at the feeing fair. The

The Main Street Lochwinnoch c. 1900.

feeing fair was held in Glasgow and farmers would find new employees there. If a farmer thought you might suit him he would discuss wages, duties, conditions etc, and the bargain would be sealed by him making a token payment, which when accepted bound you to the bargain. Sometimes the deal did not materialize and there were what was called 'run away fairs' in early December.

The constant moving was not considered a troublesome burden. Single men liked to skirt around the farms in the area, and married couples had the opportunity to move if they so wished. The housing was in a cottage or an outbuilding which was called the bothy. If girls were employed as kitchen or dairy maids they slept in the kitchen or in a

Chopping hay at Barkip Farm, Dalry (next to Beith) c. 1871. The hay was bagged and taken by rail to Glasgow for horse feed.

James Alexander (1834–1924).   *Jane Alexander (1847–1928).*

room nearby. Not unnaturally there were large numbers of illegitimate births and a social climate existed in which no one thought it very wicked to bear a bastard. It was not unusual to see a birth certificate indicating that the child was the legitimate son or daughter of so-and-so.

The hours of work and the tasks undertaken varied with the different types of land on the farms. The byremen would start at 5 a.m. with scraping down the cow stalls and washing the cows, ready to start milking at 5.30 a.m. At the same time the ploughmen fed their horses, mucked them out, groomed and harnessed them, ready to start work at 7 a.m., they having had their breakfast during this period. The ploughmen were considered the élite of the outside workers and on the large farms where there were several workers the ploughmen had their own pecking order in taking out their horses to work: the head horseman first, second horseman next, followed by the third. If the weather was suitable they worked until 6 p.m. in the summer and to darkness in the winter. The byremen generally managed to finish their long day by 6 p.m. but always checked the byre before going to bed. Seasonal workers were employed on the farms at harvest and haymaking time, and also for tattie lifting and shawing the neeps. Many were migrant workers from the Highlands or from Ireland. It is interesting to note that the lists of school attendances in Lochwinnoch in the 1880s and 1890s are full of references to low attendances during the month of August because of the children being engaged in harvest work.

East Auchengown was typical of farms in the hilly district around Lochwinnoch. Many of them were less than 100 acres and the farmer kept about twenty cows. When there was only a small family, generation usually followed generation. However, when there were large families and a spirit of adventure, some farmers became tempted, from listening to the stories of friends and relations, to move elsewhere where there would be more scope and increased prosperity. This was the prime reason for the Alexanders' decision to leave East Auchengown.

CHAPTER 2

Scottish traditions taken South

From the early 1880s to the mid-1890s there was a tremendous influx of Scotsmen to the South, especially to Essex, with some 120 to 130 farmers becoming established during that period. The reason for farms being available to let was that the traditional arable husbandry of the Eastern Counties had been badly hit by competition from cheap imports of wheat, particularly from the United States. Many native farmers had given up in despair and the landowners were desperate to obtain fresh tenants. The price of wheat in 1880 was around £10 9s. 6d. per ton, in 1890 it was £7 6s. od. and by 1900 it had dropped further to £6 3s. od. per ton (it did not rise significantly until 1914/1918, £8 to £17).

Ayrshire and Renfrewshire farmers, who had large families and were rearing twice as many potential farmers as there were farms for them, were in the meantime looking for farms elsewhere other than locally. Instead of growing cereals as the departed farmers had done they began dairying, selling hay and growing potatoes. These were the very farming practices they knew so well and they had London as a market right on their doorstep. Quite naturally, they bought in all the cereals they fed to their livestock as the price was in their favour. Their prosperity was not only attributed to the hard work that the farmer did himself, but also to their Scottish wives and daughters who were willing to do much manual work. It is often said that the only reason a Scottish farmer went back to Scotland was to bring down another Scot. They always kept in close touch with each other and what they didn't know about their neighbours wasn't really worth knowing!

These Scots loved their celebrations and get-togethers, Burns Night suppers being of particular importance. They really revelled at the sound of bagpipes as they sat at the richly decorated tables in the village hall they had hired for the evening. The piper would enter the hall dressed in his full Scottish regalia, with the chef in his pure white outfit and tall hat following; he would be carrying a large plate with a steaming hot haggis upon it. Close behind them would be another Scot, carrying the traditional bottle of whisky so they could all enjoy 'a wee dram' after the president of the evening had addressed the haggis. This address consisted of a recital of the full eight verses of Robert Burns's poem 'To a Haggis'.

To give this setting some atmosphere, I quote just the first and last verses:

> Fair fa' your honest, sonsie face,
> Great Chieftain o' the Puddin-race!
> Aboon them a'ye tak your place,
>   Painch, tripe or thairm:
> Weel are ye wordy o' a grace
>   As lang's my arm.

Piping in the haggis at a Burns Night Supper.

> Ye Pow'rs wha mak mankind your care
> And dish them out their bill o'fare,
> Auld Scotland wants nae skinking ware
>   That jaups in luggies;
> But if ye wish her gratefu' prayer,
>   Gie her a Haggis!

The toast was completed by everyone having their wee dram. The traditional food of spoonfuls of haggis, champit tatties and bashed neeps was then served, followed by a fairly regular menu. The evening concluded with Scottish dances and reels which further stirred their Scottish spirits.

The New Year was always another occasion for celebration, although, unlike in England, Christmas Day went by very quietly as it was not at that time taken as a day's holiday in Scotland. In the Scottish custom, still upheld in many places, of 'first footing' after midnight on New Year's Eve, it is not considered lucky for someone with red, white or fair hair to be the first person to call at a house in the New Year and walk over the doorstep; it has to be a dark-haired person. The visitor carries in a symbolic lump of coal to keep the fires burning, and a bottle of whisky is also taken in to wish the household good health and happiness. People often call at one another's houses right into the small hours to wish the occupants 'a guid New Year'. It is no wonder that New Year's Day has long been a holiday in Scotland, as many a person would not be fit to work anyway. It is of note that New Year's Day went by as an ordinary day in England until 1975 when it was made an official holiday.

Another long-standing tradition is the 'Show of Presents' held about a week before a wedding. It has always been a great social gathering and often takes place over two days. Friends who have sent presents and others who bring gifts with them, are shown round by the bride-to-be and by her sisters or cousins. Everything is tastefully displayed in the best room or rooms in the house, and people expect to be told who gave which present. As you can imagine, this creates some rivalry and private discussion afterwards. It is not uncommon for there to be two to three hundred presents. So often, even if you had only just heard of a bride-to-be you would give her something, or just 'a minding' as they often call smaller presents. Afternoon tea is always given, which involves the bride's mother and helpers in baking home-made scones, pancakes, crumpets, tattie scones and shortbread, all these, of course, proceeded by dainty sandwiches. It is an exhausting time for those concerned, especially the bride in writing her 'thank you' letters.

Scottish associations have been formed in all parts of the world. Their traditions are readily celebrated at every opportunity and 'locals' are invited to join in. Quite naturally, they become envious and are delighted to be included in the fold. Long may the traditions continue to be celebrated.

CHAPTER 3
The move to Home Farm, Eynsford

The Alexander family moved to Home Farm on 4 February 1892. It is unlikely to have been predicted that the family's descendants would be farming that very same land one hundred years later. It is pleasing to know that the fourth generation are now firmly settled in the driving seats—the third generation being very good back-seat drivers!

The move, or 'flitting' as the Scots call it, generated lots of discussion in the

Joseph Larter's diary entries of Eynsford events.

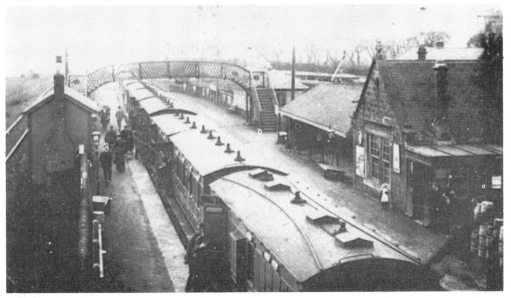

Lochwinnoch Station c. 1900. Note milk churns lower right.

planning. The incoming tenant to Auchengown was most helpful in agreeing to buy the young livestock and most of the equipment which was not going to Kent. Only fourteen of the eighteen Ayrshire cows were taken, six of the oldest heifers and Hamish, the Ayrshire bull. The milking stools, luggies (milking pails), milk cooler, churns, butter-making equipment and feeding barrows were essential dairy items to take. The chaff cutter and the mangel-wurzel shredder were equally important too.

Hay, straw and food were taken down to Lochwinnoch Station. The cattle were driven down the road, a distance of only one mile to where railway cattle trucks and other wagons were waiting in a siding. The cattle truck had a convenient compartment at one end for the stockman, in which there was a long seat and table and a viewing hole to see the cattle.

The Glasgow and South Western Railway, formed in 1850 and known as 'The Sou' West' ran as far as Carlisle. The London and North Western Railway would complete their journey south. Railways were keen to have business and provided reasonable facilities.

James Alexander travelled with his cattle. There were many relatives and local inhabitants who came to the station to wish him good luck, a safe journey and good farming in England. It was a very emotional day watching the livestock being loaded and the train leaving Lochwinnoch Station. Their joy and sorrow were accompanied by a 'wee dram' which had thoughtfully been provided.

The first stop was at Carlisle, where the livestock was unloaded at the siding, where the cows were milked and all the animals were fed, watered and given some exercise. The same routine took place at Crewe. The final unloading was at Eynsford Station, and my grandfather was more than thankful to have arrived safely at the end of the long journey. The last lap for the cattle was a walk of less than a mile down the road towards the village and through the ford of the river Darent near the picturesque Tudor Cottage. Finally, they were guided into a straw-bedded cowshed in the thatched barn at Home Farm adjacent to the road.

My grandmother and the rest of the family arrived by train the following day. They were given a similar send-off from Lochwinnoch and there were many white

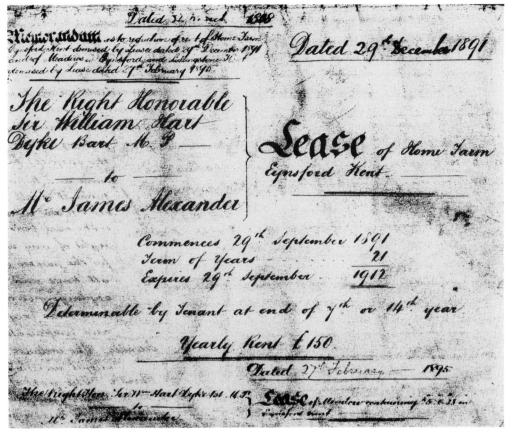

The lease title for Home Farm 29th September 1891.

handkerchiefs to wipe away the tears that morning. It was the first long train journey for the children and they were really excited, but they couldn't hide their sadness at leaving the home they had lived in since they were born. There were great promises made of coming back to visit their friends and the hope that some of them would come to England. Their luggage included some cases filled with farewell presents or 'mindings' (a lovely Scottish expression) which would be treasured as mementos of Auchengown. There was another treasure going with them. They were allowed to take their very lovable Scottish Collie sheepdog, Lassie, and although she had to travel in the guards' van, they were able to go and see her at some stations. You can just imagine what joy that companionship gave the children.

My grandfather and one of the farm men were at Eynsford Station to meet their train and had a horse and wagon and the pony and trap waiting. It had been a chilly day and there was frost that night. Everyone was tired and cold after the long journey, so the log fire burning in the kitchen on their arrival was particularly welcoming. After an excited quick scout through some of this large farmhouse, they all settled around the bare wooden kitchen table and were soon enjoying a large bowl of good Scottish porridge, made with salt, of course. No one seemed particularly hungry, having eaten large quantities of sandwiches and cakes on the train journey, so supper time passed fairly quickly and soon the children were scampering up the stairs. They had a lick and a promise for a wash and were quickly fast asleep in their new home. Tiredness eventually overtook the grown-ups' discussions, and they too were soon fast asleep on their first night at Home Farm.

Inventory & Valuation on *Home Farm* in the Parish of *Eynsford* in the County of *Kent* from *Sir W. Hart Dyke* to *Mr James Alexander*.

22nd January 1892.

Labour to Land.

10 : 0 : 0   Swine Grass   (Part of)
Ice ploughed. Wheat seed. Sowing & season.

12 : 0 : 0   Do   (Part of)
Ice ploughed. Wheat seed. sowing & season.

Young Seeds.

2 : 0 : 0   Do   (Part of)
Ice ox harrowed. Ice small harrowed. Trifolium seed sowing & season.

All the *Hay* (½ Feed & ½ Market Price)
All the *Straw* at Feed Price.
All the *Underwood* down to the Stub.
Labour to *Manure*.

We do Value the whole contained in the foregoing *Inventory* at the sum of One hundred and Thirtytwo Pounds two Shillings & Sixpence including ½ stamp & Inventory

£ 132 : 2 : 6

Inventory and valuation on Home Farm, 1892.

Home Farm house 1923.

CHAPTER 4
The settling-in period

My grandfather had made several visits from Scotland to Home Farm between September, when he took over the tenancy, and February, when he moved in. During this period preparations were made for the arrival of the animals and the equipment.

I was told that the first morning's milking was very hectic in the old barn. The dim light from the paraffin storm lanterns did not help very much in finding things in unfamiliar places and some items were not there at all. The cows were fed a mixture of crushed oats and cake which kept them fairly content during milking. My grandfather and the two farm-workers helped that morning although only one was usually at the milking. The milk was carried in covered pails on a wooden yoke to the scullery in the farmhouse. It was tipped into an overhead receiving pan and then trickled down each side of a corrugated milk-cooler, through which cold water was flowing, into 17-gallon churns.

Corrugated milk cooler and 17 gallon churn.

Cake breaker for slabs of linseed cattle cake.

Loading dung cart by thatched barn.

My grandmother was always up early in the morning and one of the first things she did was to light the kindled log fire under the copper in the corner of the scullery. Hot water would then be ready in good time for washing up the dairy dishes, milk pails and milking buckets. The kitchen stove was lit to give warmth and boil the kettle. The ever welcome bowl of porridge which had been left soaking from the night before was heated on the stove in readiness for grandfather when he came in from the milking and for the children when they came downstairs. They had a simple breakfast of porridge, a boiled egg, toast and tea.

At the finish of milking the two partly filled 17-gallon churns were taken by horse and cart to Eynsford Station. They were carried across the railway tracks by two station porters to the 'up' line for the train to Swanley. The dairyman collected the milk at the station and left two empty churns for return to Eynsford. The churns were tall and tapered with a very wide base, which made it easy to roll them along railway platforms and elsewhere. Also they were very stable whilst being transported.

On that first morning the children went outside after breakfast to explore the farm whilst their mother washed up the dairy dishes. They hadn't seen such large thatched barns before and were keen to see the cows, horses and their pony and trap. The river flowing so close by had its fascination, as did the steam engines they could hear and see on the railway not far distant. David and Jessie Greenlees and their three boys came over from Otford to help with the moving in. The cousins met for the very first time and before long, after the initial very shy period, they were having fun together. It was the beginning of a lifelong friendship. Auchengown had been rather sparsely furnished so there was not a great deal of furniture to carry in, and what there was looked quite lost in the much larger farmhouse, which had three stories and an attic as compared with the two stories in Auchengown. One can well imagine the excitement of the first day for them all.

The two farm-workers and their families lived in Home Farm cottages on the other

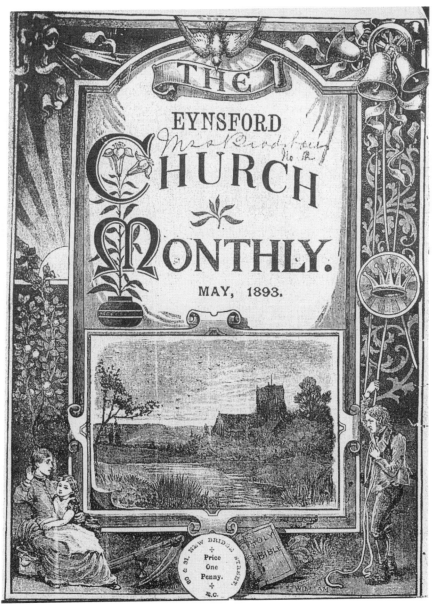

THE

EYNSFORD

CHURCH

MONTHLY.

MAY, 1893.

Church Magazine, May 1893.

side of the road from the thatched barn, one man was primarily concerned with the horses and the outside field work, whilst the other was always at the milking and looked after the livestock. There were only sixteen stalls in the barn; other cows and in-calf heifers were kept in a wooden shed close by in the yard. There was no piped water to the buildings so it was carried each day from the river. During the grazing season the cows could drink from the river which flowed through the meadows. The cowman crushed oats and mixed it with linseed cake, which came in large slabs that were broken in a crusher turned by hand, looking rather like a clothes mangle. At about midday the livestock had a feed of mangel-wurzels, which had been sliced in a cutting machine. Hay, from the barn or a stack in the field, was cut out and trussed and was fed to the animals at the end of afternoon milking. For much of the winter

THE EYNSFORD CHURCH MONTHLY.

EYNSFORD PARISH CHURCH.

The Vicar and Mrs. Hutchinson having left home for their holiday, it has been arranged that the Rev. E. A. Williams take the duty of the Parish for the last two weeks of April, and the Rev. N. Dimock for May. On the last Sunday in May sermons will be preached for the Church Pastoral Aid Society.

EYNSFORD NATIONAL SCHOOL.

On Friday evening, April 14th, there was a goodly gathering at the National School to witness the annual distribution of school prizes. The proceedings opened by a pleasing and successful entertainment, consisting of songs, recitations, etc., by the pupils, chiefly the little ones, for whom there was not room at the Annual Concert last December. Their efforts to please the audience were well received, the musical-drill coming in for special applause. Mrs. Wheeler with her usual energy, acted as leader in the various parts, and Miss N. Tydd presided at the piano. After the entertainment the Vicar addressed a few words to those present, mentioning that the prizes were given entirely for good attendance, every pupil who had attended 320 times out of a possible 431 received a prize. In each standard the value of every prize was the same, but of course the prizes assigned to the standard varied according to the seniority of the pupils. We append the names of those who were successful.

Percy Wheeler, Albert Baldwin (431), Polly Lawrence, George Turner, Richard Wheeler (429), Walter Baldwin (425), Amy Higton (424), Willie Smith, John Wellard (422), Maggie Fuller, Florrie Baldwin (420), Edward Barr (419), Edith Leigh, Leonard Smith (417), Edith King (414), Arthur Cliffe, Willie Jennings, Annie Cliffe (413), John Baldwin, Edith Smith (412), May Lawrence (405), Arthur Barber, Daisy Clout (401).

Over 350. Jane Alexander (398), Willie Alexander (397), Frank Barber, Willie Wellard (395), Alice Abbott, David Booker (392), Rose Wickenden, Kate Barber, Bertie Mason, Kate Smith (390), Winnie Stockwell, Albert Jennings (389), Fred Baldwin (387), Nellie Baldwin (382), Thomas Smith (381), Edith Goose (369), Annie Love (367), Florrie Wickenden (359), Bertie Warner, Thomas Booker (353).

Under 350. Annie Pearse, May Roberts, Fred Baldwin, Victor Barber, Charles Smith, John Wheeler, Elizabeth Ralph, Ada Ball, James Ball, Percy Luckhurst, Dot Baldwin, Caroline Wheeler, Alfred Baldwin, Jesse Kimber, Frank Barber, Maud West, James Larter, May Booker, John Gaston, Arthur Lawrence, Willie Kimber, Bertie Gaston, Alfred Gaston, Ethel Burke, Arthur Baldwin, John Johnson, Willie Baldwin, Jim Kimber, Elizabeth Love.

Eynsford National School report.

the horseman carted out the dung from the yard midden to the field. It was then spread and ploughed in. Hedge cutting was always a fallback job in the winter.

All the heifer calves that were born were reared as replacements for the herd; the bull calves were taken to market. My grandfather went to Dartford market, which was near the centre of the town at the rear of the Bull Hotel and Pub, driving the pony and cart with the calf securely netted over. It was always an opportunity to have a discussion with fellow farmers and merchants. Messrs R. & H. Strickland, who started business in Dartford in 1851 as corn merchants, were regular attenders at the Tuesday market, and my grandfather did business with them right from the start. Their offices and warehouses were in Spital Street, which was certainly different from how one sees it today.

The Alexander children went to school in Eynsford. There were two schools. The National, which they went to, was built in 1834, and the Board built in 1855 and replaced by a new school in 1894. Both schools were for boys and girls. Kelly's Post Office Directory for 1895 showed an average attendance of 93 and 81 respectively. By 1899 these averages had increased to 107 and 133. The total capacity for both schools was 265. The Alexanders found it rather difficult to understand all the English tongues at first—but equally their Scottish brogue presented some questioning by teachers and classmates alike. I am not aware of there being any school reports but they were mentioned for good attendance. Eynsford Church published a monthly magazine. In the May 1893 issue the report reads: 'On Friday evening April 14th there was a goodly gathering at the National School to witness the annual distribution of school prizes.' The prizes were given entirely for good attendance. Out of a possible 431 attendances, Jane Alexander was credited with 398 and Willie Alexander with 397. Their two sisters did not receive a mention.

Handicraft was encouraged in the village and my father and his sister Martha became very keen on woodcarving. They carved two very large oak-framed mirrors,

Christmas 1904. William, Martha, Jane and Mary Alexander.

dated 1903 and 1904, which must have taken many hours of patience. It is not surprising that they were interested in this craft as both Lochwinnoch and Beith were renowned for their high-quality furniture. It was made for both the domestic and commercial markets and was bought by many of the Clyde shipping companies for their passenger liners. Four famous ships had Lochwinnoch-made furniture on board: the *Lusitania*, the *Mauretania*, the *Queen Mary* and the *Queen Elizabeth*. My father was also interested in basket work, which was taught at the Castle Institute in Eynsford. In 1905 he received a certificate, £1 and a bronze medal for the excellence of his work.

My Aunt Martha became very ill in February 1907 and died at the young age of twenty-eight from tuberculosis. It was an extremely sad time for everyone.

In October of the same year my Aunt Jane was married to David Norton. The wedding group photograph was taken on the front lawn of Home Farm. My grandparents are in the second row just to the left and right of David Norton. My father is sitting on the lawn cross-legged.

Jane Alexander and David Norton. Wedding photograph on the lawn at Home Farm.

David Norton's corn mill by the bridge over the river Darent at Eynsford.

David Norton was a miller and corn merchant. His mill was by the bridge at Eynsford and had been built circa 1780. The grinding stones were turned by a very large water-wheel in the river Darent. The teeth in the wooden cog wheels were made of apple wood. David Norton made deliveries of animal and pet foods with his pony and cart to local farms and shops. The enamelled notices on the wall of his mill advertised Spratts Patent Dog Food and Molassine Meal. A few years later he moved to the Windmill at Kingsdown which had a much larger milling capacity. Eynsford Mill premises were used for a short period as a boot and shoe-lace factory. The business flourished so well that Mr Millen the owner moved to a larger building at Horton Kirby. The Mill House is now a private residence and three of the very old mill stones are embedded in the pathway to the front entrance.

The village green between the river, Eynsford bridge and the Tudor Cottage was a very popular place for holding village events. A Maypole dance was held there regularly each year. In 1911 Mr Elliott Till commissioned Ivor I. J. Symes, a distinguished artist, to paint the scene. This was done for the proscenium curtain of the village hall stage, the size of the painting being 20 feet long by 12 feet high. Local people are depicted in the painting, including my grandfather, James Alexander, standing on a platform at the Centre Pole dressed in green pantaloons, which contrasted with his ginger-coloured hair. He is shown playing the fiddle which he brought with him from Scotland and which he was always so delighted to play on any occasion. One of the dancers is my Aunt Mary, holding a Maypole ribbon and wearing a long blue dress. Mr Till is sitting close by on a wooden bench chatting to friends whilst listening to the music and watching the dancing. The tradition of the event continues with a May Ball, held each year in the village hall, which is a most popular occasion.

Another significant event in Eynsford was the Elizabethan Fayre, held in the village on 27 June 1914. Some of the procession assembled in the meadow behind Home Farm where my father was to be seen, wearing a black and white striped hat and jacket

The Maypole Dance on the village green, 1911.

and thigh-length stockings; with him was his sister Mary, dressed in Elizabethan costume. The whole assembly, of about two hundred people took place on the village green. Lady Emily Hart Dyke as Queen Elizabeth was the chief character and rode side-saddle on a white horse. Her coronet sat well on a mass of auburn hair while the high Medici-collar and richly bedecked costume gave a truly queenly Elizabethan aspect to the procession. An address of welcome to the Queen was given by Joe Munn, the village grocer, at the Tudor Cottage.

'Hail to thee Most Gracious Queen, fair mould of beauty, miracle of fame, on this the occasion of thy Majesty's most gracious visit to our ancient village of Eynsford. So

Preparing for the Elizabethan Fayre by the farmhouse back door.

Assembling in the meadow. William Alexander wearing striped top hat. Elizabethan Fayre 27th June, 1914.

The crowd by Eynsford bridge.

all your own desires go with thee, lady, and God bless thee with long life, honour and heart's ease.'

The assembly then processed along the High Street to the grounds of the ruins of Eynsford Castle where the Pageant was held. The event was watched by a holiday crowd estimated at between two and three thousand people. A play was enacted in the evening followed by dancing until midnight. The organizer of the event was Miss Sydney Dyke the youngest daughter of Sir William and Lady Emily Hart Dyke. She was a very independent young lady and in her early thirties defied her father's disapproval and became founder and Scoutmaster of the 1st Eynsford Scout Troop in 1912. They met in the store alongside the watchman's quarters in Oast Cottage at Lullingstone. Sydney was very much respected by the lads who had very happy times under her command. She was thus suited to marshal the Elizabethan Fayre two years later.

The residents of Eynsford enjoyed a particularly strong community spirit and there were many organizations in which they could partake. When you showed an interest and were willing to give help, you were soon enrolled on a committee. The settling in period was therefore also a period of welcome.

CHAPTER 5
William Alexander takes over

The farming system at Home Farm continued pretty well the same year-in year-out whilst my grandfather was in command. My grandmother supplied milk to people at the back door of Home Farm and the amount of milk sold steadily increased. She also sold skim milk and butter. Cream was separated three times a week; warm milk was poured into a holding container on the top of the separator which was turned by hand, and the skim milk was either sold or fed to the pig which was kept to eat up the household scraps—Scottish thriftiness—and the cream was made into butter. All the utensils for butter making were wooden and were washed in salt water before use to prevent the butter adhering to them. Once the butter was formed and the whey drained off, it was shaped using a pair of thin wooden bats with serrated faces, called Scotch Hands. The butter shapes were oblong, of various sizes, and the rounds were impressed with carved wooden butter stamps having a Scotch Thistle design. Small butter balls were made specially for parties and Sunday teas. Ethel Darby, a well-known resident in Eynsford, remembers as a very small child going round to Home Farm and buying skim milk for one penny a pint. She said that Mrs Alexander always wore a long white apron and had her hair in a bun.

In 1908, my father, at the age of twenty-five, took over the farming responsibilities, while his father took a less active role. He had ideas to increase the size of the dairy herd, to acquire additional land and buildings when opportunity arose, and eventually to start a retail milk round.

In 1912 the landlords, the Hart Dyke family, built a new cowshed for thirty cows at Home Farm, with some Scottish characteristics incorporated into the design. A glazed pipe came through the wall to each pair of cows and gave good fresh air ventilation, and each cow had a large glazed rectangular feed trough. The roof was timber-boarded and covered with slates and had vented canopies in the ridge. The outside appearance of the cowshed, which is now used for calf-rearing, remains today much the same as it was in 1912, having miraculously survived the bombing in 1940, the 1987 hurricane and the 1990 wind storms. Many of the adjacent buildings were destroyed by bombs and fires.

Once the new cowshed was ready for use, more Shorthorn cows were bought. Some were from Henry Steven, an uncle who farmed at Hurst Farm, Crockham Hill, and others from James Fife, another Scotsman farming at Yaldham, Kemsing. The only trace of the Ayrshire cows brought from Scotland were those cows bred to shorthorn bulls.

The landlord offered my father more land to rent in 1912. The area was increased to 158 acres and a new lease granted in my father's name for twenty-one years. A further 56 acres were added in 1915 with an 18-year lease.

31

James age 4 learns to pedal. A 17 gallon churn and milk churn barrow 1927.

During the 1914–1918 war years, there was an increase in the demand for home-grown food. The prices for milk, cereals and potatoes improved substantially, and cabbages and savoys were grown to sell to the London markets. Profits were then available to make investment purchases. The first of these was six acres of land and buildings at Little Mote in 1917. This consisted of a large barn and two bungalows on one side of the river with a bridge to the grazing meadows on the other side. This purchase provided additional summer grazing and winter accommodation for the increased herd.

By 1918 it seemed that the time was right to start a retail milk round and enquiries were made for a suitable man. Mrs Gaston, who lived in Willow Terrace in the village, said her son Arthur was interested. He had joined the Army in 1914 but was discharged soon afterwards with a valvular disease of the heart. He was working in a slaughterhouse in Cox Heath but was not at all happy in the job. Arthur, Emily and their two children moved into one of the bungalows at Little Mote. Two years later they moved to a wooden bungalow called Pagecot built from ex-Army huts on a piece of land which had been bought next to the barn at Home Farm.

Arthur started the milk round with the pony, Kitty, and float. He went along

Eynsford High Street to Farningham and back along Sparepenny Lane. The milk was carried on the float in a churn fitted with a brasss tap and a half-pint measure was used to fill the customers' jugs or cans. The price was two pence a pint. Farmers were paid eight pence per gallon in the summer, and eleven pence in winter for milk supplied to the dairies. So retailing had quite a useful margin. Milk in Scotland in the 1890s was fivepence and sixpence a gallon.

The milk-round sales gradually increased, and glass bottles with 'Home Farm, Eynsford' printed on them were eventually used. This required a simple milk-bottling machine which was hand-operated and filled four bottles at a time. Bottle-washing became another seven-days-a-week job. Two of Arthur Gaston's children, David and Dolly, came and helped before they went to school. They were up at twenty-to-six and made deliveries to Bower Lane and Crockenhill Lane. When my brother James and I were old enough we enjoyed doing deliveries at weekends and during school holidays. We used a tricycle with a built-in box. It was rather hard pedalling up-hill carrying the load, but it was great fun free-wheeling down-hill back home again.

In the afternoon, after a two-hour lunch break and a snooze, Arthur would chaff some hay and mix it with crushed oats for Kitty's nosebag on the round next morning. The pony was loved by everyone, especially the children, and knowing the round so well would stop and start almost without a word of command. Arthur helped with the afternoon milking which started at three o'clock. He had a very busy seven days a week job. His holidays consisted of taking the afternoon off, but never the mornings.

There was another milk round in the village, started by Bert Brice in 1908. He kept his few Shorthorn cows in a shed by the side of the Five Bells Public House, which his family had run since before the 1850s. The grazing was in Harrow meadow behind the pub. The cows were driven round by Elizabeth Cottages and up Bower Lane to the fields; they also grazed the Common Meadow, now used as a cricket field. Reg Morgan, known to us all, would as a schoolboy drive these cows from the Common Meadow through the river at Eynsford bridge, along the High Street and back to their shed at the Five Bells.

After the first few years of being the farmer in control, my father could foresee prospects for further expansion. Although it only needed one person to run the farm, he knew it was always helpful to have two brains to run a successful business. He believed it was the right time to take action and to put that theory into practice. To do so, he visited Scotland much more frequently!

CHAPTER 6
Back to Scotland for a wife

'I f you are looking for a farm go to the East. If you are looking for a wife go to the West.' Although my father was brought up in Kent, he still took heed of that old Scottish saying and courted a lassie in the West. Her name was Mary Allan and she had two older brothers, John and George. Her father farmed at Southridgehill, Beith, the neighbouring town to Lochwinnoch. There was a dairy herd of 32 Ayrshire cows on the 103-acre farm, part of which was cropped with oats and neeps for feeding the cattle. The only income was from milk and livestock. My mother helped with the milking and the washing up of the dairy dishes. She was keen on studying practical subjects and obtained certificates in Dairying (1910–11), Art and Needlework (1911) and Cookery (1912–13). Although I am not aware of any certificates, I am quite sure she must have received some commendation too for the neatness of her handwriting, her bookkeeping and general tidiness, qualities she continued to instil into my brother, my sister and me during the whole of her life. The Allan family were well known for their tidiness which in local circles was called the 'Allan tidiness disease'. As one example, the wee stone chippings on the road down to the farm and around the house were raked over at least once a week, Saturday mornings being a must. The place had to look 'real snod' for the unexpected visitors who seemed to call most weekends either for a wee blether or the very popular card game, nap.

My father and mother were married at Southridgehill on 25 April 1919. The Minister conducted the wedding ceremony in the bride's home, which was quite customary in Scotland at that time. There were two bridesmaids—Maggie Boyd, a cousin and farmer's daughter, and Martha McIlwraith, a schoolteacher and friend since their own schooldays. Jack Steven, a cousin of my father, was best man. His parents were farming near Westerham in Kent, having left Scotland in 1887. The bridesmaid Maggie Boyd and Jack Steven married on 22 September the same year. Both sets of newly-weds then farmed within eleven miles of one another and remained lifelong friends, consulting each other's wisdom and experiences.

After the honeymoon my parents occupied Home Farm. Their parents and Aunt Mary moved to The Priory in Eynsford, just up the road opposite Eynsford Paper Mill. My father had made the arrangements in good time. A character reference of him was given by Mr Hodsoll to the owner, Mrs Mary Apps.

The Priory was built in 1681. Documents of 1707 state that part of it had been a public house. In that lease, to one John Dowling, he was described as being the keeper of the Red Lion, barn, stable, orchard and two acres of land. The interesting wording of the 1763 lease is given in Appendix I.

Elliott Downs Till, who was a great benefactor of Eynsford, lived at The Priory before my grandparents from 1906 until his death in September 1917 aged

Moving to The Priory: Quinnells Pantechnicon

eighty-one. His sister, Elizabeth Till, had the lease from Mrs Mary Apps from 1886 until her death in March 1917 at the age of seventy-eight.

Mr Till made a very spectacular arrival at The Priory about which George Eves of Eynsford wrote.

It was a brisk morning in 1906 when I stood watching a diminutive steam tractor struggling up Priory Lane with a large pantechnicon in tow, when I should have been chanting multiplication tables in the Council school half a mile away. Large gilt block letters on the side of the van proclaimed it belonged to a Mr Quinnell of Sevenoaks and that indicated it must be a person of some substance as villagers always borrowed old Tom Baldwin's coal cart. Watching steam engines was compulsory for me. I stood in silent admiration as the furniture van was shunted back in the drive of the imposing residence I knew to be 'The Priory', where both the pantechnicon and engine were securely blocked up. Only then did the 'furniture bumpers' remove their bowler hats and don the regulation green baize aprons. It then crossed my mind that I should be late for school again and that would mean trouble. Samuel Woolley, my schoolmaster, had a way of making the punishment fit the crime, hence I had to write a hundred lines after school . . . 'Mr Quinnell's men can unload furniture without my help.' At tea time at home that night our newest inhabitant was discussed but nobody could shed any light about him, not even my ageing Aunts Dora and Agnes who were village newshounds.

A week elapsed before the mystery was solved, then my schoolmaster presented a very distinguished looking gentleman. Immaculately dressed, tall, bearded, upright bowler-hatted, he was complete with rolled umbrella, Gladstone bag and spats. We all stood up and he was introduced as Mr Elliott Downs Till. He turned out to be a man with a mission in search of things to put right. In no time he was berating the village for litter in the streets, cigarette packets in the gutters, untidy front gardens and gates left to swing in the wind. He called for our co-operation

ESTABLISHED 1830.

WILLIAM HODSOLL.
(JAMES HODSOLL)
LAND AGENT, SURVEYOR & AUCTIONEER.

Telephone No. 7 Farningham.

FARNINGHAM,
KENT.
18ᵗʰ March 1919

Dear Madam,

"The Priory. Eynsford.

Mr Percy Jepson (who at present holds the lease of this property) has desired me to ask your consent to his assigning the lease to Mr William Alexander of Home Farm. Eynsford. Kent. I enclose the Bankers reference in reply to my enquiry as to his financial position which is quite satisfactory. & personally I have known Mr Alexander many years, he holds a large farm under Sir Wm Hart Dyke, & has a good reputation in the district. I understand that he requires "The Priory" for his parents who wish to live near to him.

Yours respectfully.
Wm Hodsoll

Mr Apps.
7 Mordon Terrace.
Tunbridge Wells.

and when he left each of us a brand-new penny, he was assured of our full co-operation and thereafter front gates were well secured.

I am sure Mr Eves did not have a hundred lines to write in 1919 when my grandparents arrived at The Priory. They had lived at Home Farm for twenty-seven years and The Priory was a suitable home in which they could enjoy retirement. It was only a short distance from the farm and still within the Parish of Eynsford.

Beith School Board.

ACADEMY CONTINUATION CLASSES,

CLASS CERTIFICATE   SESSION 1910 –11

Mary Allan

has satisfactorily attended the classes in

Art Needlework   (1ˢᵗ Year)

and has been awarded this *First Class Certificate of Merit*

on the results of her work during the Session

Thos Smith   Chairman

W Stewart   Joint–Clerk

W Osler   Head Master

This Certificate is issued in respect of the syllabus of class-work and under the regulations stated on the back hereof

Mary Allan's School Certificate for Art and Needlework 1910–11 and for Cookery 1912–13

Beith School Board.

ACADEMY CONTINUATION CLASSES,

CLASS CERTIFICATE   SESSION 1912 –13.

Mary Allan

has satisfactorily attended the classes in

Cookery

and has been awarded this *First Class Certificate of Merit*

on the results of her work during the Session

Thos Smith Chairman

W Stewart Clerk

W Osler Head Master

This Certificate is issued in respect of the syllabus of class-work and under the regulations stated on the back hereof

CHAPTER 7
Two heads are better than one

By 1990 many farmers with large or small acreages were using a computer in their office as part of the farm management. Children were being taught from quite an early age at school how to use a computer, and when one required some information, the automatic response was to 'ask the computer'.

From April 1919, the computer at Home Farm was my mother. As a young wife, well schooled in Scotland, she was eager to play her part in helping her husband to 'make a go' of the farming at Eynsford. The very high standard which my father achieved was as much due to the meticulous book-keeping ability of my mother, as to his own contributions.

In 1920 there were 214 acres being farmed with leases expiring in 1933, and 80 acres with a yearly tenancy. The milking herd was 32 cows and there were also an equal number of young stock. Besides grass for grazing and haymaking, oats, wheat, potatoes, cabbages and mangel-wurzels were grown. The retail milk round sales were increasing. Daily and weekly totals of retail and wholesale milk sales were kept. Words like 'cash flow' were not used then, but my mother always had income and expenditure at her finger tips.

The dairy herd was the hub of the farming operation and improvements were always being sought, and a plan was evolved to breed a herd free of tuberculosis. Bovine tuberculosis was important for two main reasons. First, its presence impeded the application of new methods of husbandry, breeding and feeding which were being developed to increase herd productivity; and secondly, although only a comparatively small proportion of affected cows had infection in the udder, those which did could transmit tuberculosis to people drinking raw milk. There were, therefore, very good reasons for aiming to control the disease. In 1921, in the absence of a national scheme, my father had his cows tested privately. This revealed a high proportion of reactors.

The test at that time involved injecting the cow with a test substance, tuberculin, and reading the temperature of the cow at frequent intervals in the 24 hours following. A more accurate test was later evolved, in which the cows were injected with an improved form of tuberculin into the skin and skin measurements were taken at 48 and 72 hours. This improved method was used when the Ministry of Agriculture's Attested Herd Scheme was launched in 1935. Some of the improved experimental work was carried out on my father's cows by Dr Dalling, then a professor at Cambridge University, later Sir Thomas Dalling, Chief Veterinary Officer of the Ministry of Agriculture.

Although cows may have given a positive reaction to the test, their calves were, in the majority of cases, born free of infection and, as previously mentioned, the milk of most cows was uninfected. It was therefore possible to develop a scheme of control by moving calves soon after birth to a 'clean' farm. But, as every good stockman knows, it

38

is essential that calves during their first 24 hours of life be given colostrum and the antibodies it provides. The very slight risk that they might be infected at that stage had therefore to be taken.

The opportunity to enact such a control scheme came in September 1922 when Sir William Hart Dyke of Lullingstone offered my father a 21-year tenancy of Bower and Park House Farm, Eynsford. This he accepted. There was a farmhouse, three cottages and many buildings in various states of repair. An accommodating rent of £318 16s. 6d. was paid for the 483 acres. The land was mainly stiff and heavy, not easy to work, and there were several acres of woodland. Five tuberculin-tested Shorthorn cows were bought and their milk used to rear these 24-hour old calves. George Pavitt, the cowman, faithfully milked the cows and fed the calves. He was extremely proud of his calves and always enjoyed showing and talking to people about them.

In March of the same year, another farm was taken. This was New Barn Farm, Lullingstone. An annual rent of £91 10s. od. was agreed for the 61 acres and a lease of eleven years. There was a cottage, a cowshed for fifteen cows and a substantially built brick barn. New Barn had been previously farmed by the landlord, Sir William Hart Dyke.

My father bought his first Friesian cows in 1910 but they did not prove to be a success as their butterfat was too low. However, with the tenancy of another dairy farm, he was determined to try again.

In 1921 he became a member of The British Friesian Cattle Society which was formed at The Royal Show held at Gloucester in 1909. The Society's first President was General HRH Prince Christian of Schleswig-Holstein KG GCVO, from 1910 to 1913. Volume I of the *Herd Book* was published in 1912. The introduction gave the results of an analysis of the average daily yield of fat in the milk of eleven dairy breeds. This was supplied by the US Department of Agriculture. The dominance of the Holstein-Friesian is evident.

Many Butter-Test Competitions, in which all breeds have taken part, have been won by Holstein cattle. Bulletin No. 75, Bureau of Animal Industry of the U.S. Department of Agriculture, seems to show that the Holstein-Friesian leads all breeds as butter cows:

SUMMARY OF ANALYSES OF SAMPLES OF MILK FROM PURE-BRED COWS

Breed.	Fat Test.		Records of Yield.		
	No. of cows.	Fat in milk per cent.	No. of cows.	Av. daily milk yield. lbs.	Av. daily fat yield. lbs.
Holstein-Friesian	502	3.30	493	48.9	1.61
Guernsey	67	4.87	53	28.9	1.41
Jersey	164	5.13	153	24.5	1.26
Brown Swiss ...	14	3.77	14	37.3	1.41
Shorthorn	43	3.58	39	31.9	1.14
French-Canadian ...	5	3.99	5	27.0	1.08
Ayrshire	33	3.85	18	27.7	1.07
Red Poll	15	3.84	15	26.6	1.02
Devon	28	4.64	25	11.8	.55
Polled Jersey ...	5	4.66	5	22.9	1.07
Dutch Belted ...	5	3.40	5	27.2	.92

The Society has changed its name several times as the influence of the Holstein waned and waxed.

	Membership
1909 The British Holstein Cattle Society	9
1914 The British Holstein-Friesian Cattle Society	352
1918 The British Friesian Cattle Society	801
1971 The British Friesian Cattle Society of Great Britain & Ireland	13,526
1988 The Holstein-Friesian Society of Great Britain & Ireland	13,237

In 1922 a new herd at New Barn Farm was started with eleven pedigree Friesian cows. They were the first foundation cows of the 'Eynsford' herd of pedigree Friesians. The first heifer calf to be registered in the Friesian Herd Book was Eynsford Belle, born 8 November 1922: sire, Ickenham Pensioner; dam, Thorpe Barberry. The first bull calf to be registered was Eynsford Duncan, born 4 February 1923: sire, Hedges Second Series; dam, Kingswood Doris. The first bull used at New Barn was Kingswood Goldfinder. He was sired by Kingswood (imported) Yrite, one of forty bulls and twenty pedigree Friesian cows imported from Holland in 1914. Kingswood was the prefix of Mr Horace Hale's herd at Findon, Sussex.

Besides the acquisition of two farms in 1922, other important events took place. Fourteen acres of land, known as Furlongs Farm, Eynsford, were bought in June. The land lay between Sparepenny Lane and the river Darent, and between the Common Meadow (now the Cricket Field) and Little Mote. This joined on to land at Little Mote purchased in 1917. In September a further two acres were purchased at the top side of Sparepenny Lane.

The soil at Furlongs Farm was very fertile and ten acres of fruit were planted in December 1922. This was a new venture for the Alexanders. The Greenlees cousins, then at Sittingbourne, were growing large acreages of apples—a reason to have a go.

The first member of the third generation of the Alexanders was born in October that year—my brother James. It is Scottish tradition to name the first-born son after the grandfather on the paternal side, and the first-born daughter after the grandmother on the maternal side. It is understood that baby James was present at the ceremony of planting the first tree, albeit viewing it from his pram! The apple varieties planted were Bramley, Worcester and Newton Wonder and these were interplanted with blackcurrants and gooseberries. In 1928 the orchard was entered for the Plantations and Orchards Competition: 1st Prize and Challenge Cup were won for the Young Fruit Plantation, and 1st Prize and Challenge Cup for the best Blackcurrants—the Gooseberries ranked only 3rd prize.

Jack Turner, one of the longest-serving and faithful employees, planted and nurtured this orchard, tending it just like a mother would fuss over her child. He began work at Home Farm in 1916. When he left school at the age of fourteen in 1905 he worked at Lullingstone Castle as a gardener and earned six shillings for an 80-hour week. His experience there and his interest in fruit trees remained with him throughout his life, and he obtained tremendous job satisfaction from all the work he did. I spent many days with him learning how to prune apple trees. Towards the end of the day he would say, 'Willie, we had better have a look and see what the enemy says.' He would then pull his pocket watch out of his waistcoat and so often said, 'Surely it's not that time already?' He would continue pruning even when it snowed and I was feeling quite perished. I just had to wait for him to look at 'the enemy'. He was tough and very hardy.

There were no buildings at Furlongs Farm in which to store and pack fruit. As one would be needed, several 1914–1918 ex-army huts were purchased. A very large shed was built, 90 foot long by 40 foot wide with an eaves height of 11 foot 6 inches. The construction was 8 foot timber studding on a 3 foot 6 inch-wall and weatherboard

R.E.G. Brown's No 2 Lorry with Hop Pockets for London, 1930.

cladding. This was the first of many buildings my father constructed throughout his life. It remains in good order sixty-eight years later.

Following this multitude of happenings during 1922 there was consolidation for the next three years. In September 1925 another farm was rented. This was Manor Farm, Farningham, which Mr Murray Wood of Swanley had been farming. The 83 acres were let on a 21-year lease at the annual rent of £200. The landlord, the Right Honourable Earl Bathurst of Cirencester, granted permission in the lease 'for the conversion of part of the barn into a Cow House'. Four pedigree Friesian cows were purchased in November from Lord Rayleigh's Terling herd and seventeen shorthorn cows were added during the following ten months. The inventory and valuation for the out-going tenant showed that the cropping included 23 acres of winter and spring oats and nine acres of cabbages. There were stacks of clover and grass hay.

In 1922 Manor Farm suffered considerable disruption while the A20 by-pass road to Farningham was being built. There was a six-mile section of road building from Ruxley Corner to the Kennels, one mile beyond Farningham. This was a part of the Ministry of Transport's Arterial Road Scheme for the employment of London ex-servicemen after the 1914-1918 war. The contractors were Holloway Bros (London) and the project took 500 men eighteen months to build. Special trains were run from London and back each day for their transportation. When they were working more than two miles from the nearest station, they were taken in lorries to the railway—otherwise they walked. The road making involved deep cuttings from Pedham Place to where it crossed the road to Dartford at Farningham. The excavated chalk made the road embankment across Manor Farm fields. An arched skew bridge was built over the river Darent and a second bridge over the right of way from Farningham to Horton Kirby. The road was opened to traffic on 3 August 1923 by Mrs Ashley, wife of Colonel Wilfred Ashley, MP, Parliamentary Secretary, Ministry of Transport.

Granny Jane Alexander's tea party at The Priory.
Aunt Mary with the twins Mary and William June 1925.

My grandfather died on 2 January 1924 at the age of eighty-nine. My father had the 'flu at that time and was, he said, only just able to raise his head out of bed to see the cortège passing the window. James Alexander had seen the foundation stone he laid in 1891 well and truly built upon for thirty-two years. 'As one life ends another begins': my twin sister Mary and I were born on 17 March 1924. This good news was greeted by a farming friend of my father's with the words, 'You've got two for the price of one!' I started life with good manners by saying 'Ladies first', so my sister was the first born.

A piece of land of an acre and a half, just beyond Home Farm on the road towards the railway viaduct, was bought in 1926. My father built a bungalow there, appropriately named 'Meadow View' for his ageing mother and his sister Mary. Bricks were hard to come by at that time and he bought a barge-load of Belgian bricks, which were also used to build two bungalows for Mr Reg Brown and two houses at Riverside, Eynsford—all from the same barge-load.

Reg Brown's father farmed at Pedham Place, Swanley, but apart from driving the tractor Reg disliked farming. He started a lorry contracting business in 1922 when the A20 road was being constructed at Farningham Hill. From this he obtained considerable work. He met my father at that time and my father gave him business carting greenstuff to the London markets, and wheat and barley to R. & H. Strickland, the corn merchants at Dartford. Mr Brown bought one and a half acres of land in Priory Lane in 1926 where he built the two bungalows, for his brother and himself. There was sufficient space too for parking his lorry. The No. 1 lorry was a Hallford, built by Halls of Dartford in 1928. It had solid rubber tyres and the photo shows it loaded with 52 pockets of hops from Mr Roger's farm at Maplescombe, Farningham en route to the Hop Warehouses in the Boro High Street, London.

My grandmother, Jane Alexander, lived for only two years after she moved to Meadow View, dying on 12 October 1928, aged eighty-one. Aunt Mary continued to stay there until she died on 12 October 1943, aged sixty-seven.

My grandparents had seen many changes in Eynsford particularly with the intervention of the First World War. They had become well known in the village and their continuing strong Scottish accent baffled many a person during conversation. They had been pioneers of a small colony of Scots who had settled along the Darent Valley.

CHAPTER 8
Other people's stories

Little Mote Garage

The building at Little Mote was no longer required for the winter housing of young stock after New Barn, Bower and Manor Farms were rented. Another use for the empty building was needed.

The Kent Education Committee advertised in August 1927 for tenders for the conveyance by bus of pupils to and from school, morning and afternoon. Mr C. M. Hever submitted a tender and was more than delighted to know that his was accepted. The contract started on 1 September and he bought a second-hand W & G Bus which ran on solid rubber tyres. The following year he used 20-seater Bean buses, which had pneumatic tyres much to the children's delight and comfort. Mr Hever was looking for garage accommodation and my father offered him the building at Little Mote. It was, however, far too low to permit entry of the buses. So with numerous jacks and plenty of helping hands, the building was safely raised bodily three feet from the ground and concrete walls were built upon which the old wooden structure was securely fixed.

The Darenth Bus Service expanded through the years to fourteen buses. In 1952 Coronation garage was built opposite Peter Gee's grocery shop, and Mr Hever moved there. Stanley Forward who had worked for R.E.G. (Reg) Brown started his own lorry

Mr Hever's buses garaged at Little Mote, 1930.

The 1928 Bean Bus.

contracting business and he used Little Mote Garage as it became known. There was however still a farming interest there. From the summer of 1946 we kept a year-old bull, Royal Hilkeejan, and a cow there in a specially constructed loose box and bull pen at the back of the garage. Royal Hilkeejan was one of the first bulls in the country from which semen was collected for artificial insemination. Ministry regulations required that the bull be kept in complete isolation from any other stock, and this building was an ideal place. Diana Clarke, a Land Girl at the time, looked after both animals with loving care.

N. K. Denham

Our trading with the agricultural merchants Wm Lillico and Sons started before 1929. Mr Keith Denham, now the senior director of the company, relates how at the age of twenty-two he was first introduced to Mr William Alexander in 1929. This was at the Corn Exchange, Mark Lane in London, which my father occasionally attended. Lionel Lillico introduced his nephew Keith Denham whereupon my father said, 'You'd better send the boy to see me.'

A week later, in some fear and trepidation, he rang the wire-operated front door bell of Home Farm. Mrs Alexander answered and this was the first of a lifetime of calls at Home Farm but afterwards always at the back door. My father bought 'straights' for the home mixing of cattle foods, and Keith Denham called regularly every two weeks after attending Ashford Market.

At a visit early in 1930 Mr Denham vividly remembers meeting two other farmers at Home Farm, Jack Steven and Jim Greenlees, both cousins of my father and dairy farmers at Westerham. It was tea time and good chatter ensued. My mother's teas were always enjoyed by the many visitors who came to Home Farm. Home-baked soda scones, tattie scones, pancakes, and fruit cake or a sponge were her Scottish specialities. When the tea-time talk changed to business that afternoon, 'the boss', as

Mr Denham called my father, told him that he had better send a D.O. (delivery order) to R.E.G. Brown for six tons Garterns gluten. Jack Steven piped up with 'Send me four tons,' and Jim Greenlees with 'Send me two tons.' Young Keith was highly delighted with these two new orders. Many other farmers were invited to tea when Mr Denham was expected to call at Home Farm and he has always been grateful to the boss for these introductions.

A further introduction was the buying of Scotch Seed Potatoes, of which Keith Denham had no experience. So the boss sent him to Scotland giving the names of three people to contact: Mr Baron at Brechin, Mr Peebles of Perth, and Mr Lyburn in Glasgow. Keith asked each of them for the price of 80 tons of seed Majestic to be told by the first two, 'Weel, Mr Denham, we'll be letting you know.' Following some persuasion, Mr Lyburn gave a price. On his return Keith reported to the boss who said, 'Well, you've done well, boy.' This was the beginning of a large trade in Scotch seed potatoes for Keith Denham.

A few years later Keith drove the boss to Scotland in his open-top car. The first scheduled stop was Penrith for lunch (2.30 p.m.). My father went to see Willie McKendrick at Kilmacolm, the Dennistown herd and John Houston, near Paisley the Royal herd, to buy Friesian bull calves for rearing. Keith Denham's visits to Scotland were not only to buy potatoes. In 1937 he married Shena Hendry from Bridge of Weir. William Alexander always maintained good connections with Scotland and imparted a wealth of information to others.

F. C. Hynard – Ben Brice

My father was always keen to help young farmers or other farmers new to the district. One of his early 'pupils' was Mr F. C. Hynard who previously had a successful draper's shop in London, but had developed serious trouble in both lungs and was advised by his doctor to live and work in the country. Lower Austin Lodge Farm was vacant and derelict, the previous tenants, Messrs Cannell's, large nurserymen growing shrubs, plants and fruit trees, having gone bankrupt. In 1920 Mr Hynard rented the farm of 268 acres from Sir William Hart Dyke at an annual rent of £219. He made a success of his farming having closely followed many of Home Farm ideas. He lived to be ninety-six years old—the doctor's advice in 1920 was certainly proved. My father and mother were often invited to Mr and Mrs Hynard's house for an evening coffee. I remember being told one morning after the evening's farming discussions that Mr Hynard's enthusiasm and concentration had become the better of him during his quest for information. After drinking up his own cup of coffee, he drank my father's coffee too and what's more, being oblivious of the fact, he then asked my father if he would like a second cup. My father thought that the least said the better. So he went home feeling rather thirsty. By his nature Mr Hynard was very much a hard business man. If you asked if you could have a cabbage or a savoy for dinner from his field, he would tell you to take one as long as it was pigeon pecked (they were unmarketable). Little did the Alexanders realize that later they would be farming Lower Austin Lodge Farm. This was from 1971 after Mr Hynard's youngest son Gordon suddenly died in June 1970.

Ben Brice, who had a milk round in Eynsford, delivered to Lower Austin Lodge Farm and this was always the last call of the day. Ben related the story of how he truly blotted his copy book one day with Mr Hynard. Bert Brice, Ben's father, had told him to hurry home early one particular day. The mare on the milk float, said Ben, could fairly put a move-on, especially when heading for home. The pony that day was really

Ben Brice and his pony milk float.

pacing it out after leaving the farm particularly down-hill round the last bend, when, to his alarm, Ben saw Mr Hynard's car stopped in the middle of the road whilst he talked to his foreman Jack White. Ben knew he couldn't pull up so went straight into the back of his car. 'He called me all the names he could think of.' 'I'll report you to the police,' said Mr Hynard. A couple of days later when Ben came out of The Castle, having had his evening drink, a sergeant and the local policeman were there. 'We've come to take you in,' they said, to which Ben in his polite manner replied, 'That will be a pleasure.' 'We've had a report of you driving dangerously.' 'Oh!' said Ben. 'Mr Hynard, I suppose.' 'Yes,' they said. 'Well, we're not taking you in but are cautioning you for driving with undue care and attention.'

Mr Hynard wouldn't speak to Ben for some while afterwards until he was making his four seasons film of Eynsford. He said to Ben, 'You're a bit of a village character; I want to film you.' His shot showed Ben delivering milk to the farm with his pony and milk float. He asked him to drop a bottle of milk on the roadway. The bottle broke and the milk ran across the road. In editing the film Mr Hynard added a section to it which

New Barn farm bridge after the floods, 1968.

showed a reverse of the incident—that is, the milk running back into the bottle and the bottle jumping up into Ben's hand. This film was shown on BBC TV and remains in their archives. A duplicate film is kept and often shown by Eynsford Village Society.

Mildred, Lady Hart Dyke

On the 16 September 1968 the entire Darent Valley was flooded by heavy rain unprecedented since circa 1840. There was too much water in the river Darent to flow through the arches of the bridges and the strength of the river swept away several bridges including one at Otford, one by Lullingstone Castle, one for New Barn Farm and the Metropolitan Water Board bridge close to Eynsford railway viaduct.

We, as tenants of New Barn Farm since 1922, used the bridge every day for access to the farm from Lullingstone Lane. Our landlord Sir Oliver Hart Dyke agreed to provide a replacement bridge. Unfortunately he was ill shortly afterwards and his wife Mildred, Lady Hart Dyke undertook to make the enquiries. Her eventual success in replacing the bridge was the result of a 'chance encounter', as she described it.

She met a Royal Engineer Officer at a dinner party, who during the conversation said that the Army sometimes put down a bailey bridge as part of an exercise and that this cost nothing. He advised her to get in touch with Colonel Harris, at the RE barracks at Chatham. An 'on site' meeting at New Barn Farm took place with the Royal Engineers, the Water Board and a few other interested people. The discussion was followed by a softening-up sherry party at the Castle. But unfortunately to no avail. The Water Board were adamant that the bridge should be built on abutments and the Army would not consider putting down a bailey bridge unless it was on piles. This deadlock was a tremendous disappointment.

Through further enquiries, Lady Hart Dyke learned that bailey bridges over the Rhine, the Danube and the Tigris had been built on piles and had withstood tanks and entire armies over them. And to add ammunition to her guns she also learned that a bridge on the Sevenoaks By-pass built on abutments had been swept away by floods. With this valuable knowledge Lady Hart Dyke finally convinced Major Taylor of the Water Board to allow her to build a bridge on piles.

The death next year, 1969, of Sir Oliver reinforced the need for a bridge. Lady Hart Dyke realized that New Barn Farm would have to be sold to provide money to pay death duties in due course and that for the farm to realize its full market value, a bridge was essential. She obtained an estimate from a Dartford firm of engineers to build a bridge. It came to £4,500. But there was not the money in the 'kitty', as Lady Hart Dyke put it, and in her inimitable manner she said, 'I'll have another throw of the dice.'

It was some time later that her estate manager informed her that the bailey bridge over the river Darent at Otford would be moved when the new bridge was complete. What was the chance of obtaining the bridge? Lady Hart Dyke made enquiries with the Kent County Council at Maidstone. They directed her to the Ministry of the Environment in London, on whom she called the following day without an appointment. She talked her way into their office and was received courteously but was informed that the bridge was the concern of the Ministry of Defence and that she should see a Mr Halstead. So Lady Hart Dyke pursued her cause. Mr Halstead listened intently to her story of woe and agreed to make the necessary arrangements for the bridge to be re-erected at New Barn Farm. She returned to Lullingstone Castle very tired but highly elated with the results of the day. However, two days later misfortune unhappily ensued through the lack of communications. The Ministry of the Environment had whisked the bridge away one night to Scotland before the Ministry of Defence had issued their orders.

Shaken but not easily put off and still very determined, she decided to have one final 'throw of the dice', and made a further contact with the Army at Chatham. They gave their assurance that a bailey bridge would eventually be available. She was really delighted and sent for my brother James and me. We readily agreed to construct the concrete piles free of charge. We were also happy to know that there were prospects of having a bridge once again. Some months elapsed before the long-awaited news came. Then the Army phoned Lady Hart Dyke to say that a bridge was available and an army exercise would take place on the night of 17 August to put down her bridge.

At ten o'clock the next morning Lady Hart Dyke went down to see how they were getting on.

To her amazement there was the perfect bridge looking as if it had been there all its life, but there was no sign of the Army. She was told by 'the locals' that the men were up and off at first light, taking their kitchens, tents and equipment with them. No mess, not even a piece of paper, was left. Lady Hart Dyke's utter joy was marked by sending a card with a brief message to her stepson, Guy Hart Dyke, in the South of France: 'August 18th 1972. I stood on the bridge at midday.'

Back at Lullingstone Castle, Mildred, Lady Hart Dyke with a glass of sherry held firmly in her hand, toasted all those people who had helped her—the toast being 'To the Battle of the Bridges'.

R. & H. Strickland, Dartford

In 1851 Mr Samuel Strickland bought a corn merchanting business from John Willding in Spital Street. He was succeeded by his sons Roland and Harold in 1891, with whom my grandfather James Alexander did a small amount of business.

A Mail Coach at The Royal Victoria Bull Hotel, Dartford.

In those very early days there were at least twelve water-mills on the river Darent between Sevenoaks and Dartford, nine of which were flour mills. My uncle, David Norton, owned one of the mills by the bridge over the Darent in Eynsford. Bread was made with all English wheat and its quality varied greatly according to the weather at harvest time. The whole population therefore knew the effect of a wet summer by the deterioration of a loaf of bread.

Once wheat was being imported from America, mills were established at ports and Strickland's purchased Town Wharf Waterside, Dartford, in 1898. The result was that the Darent mills gradually ceased being used. The last sack of flour to be milled was at Farningham in 1900 by William Moore. He sold his flour to several bakers in the East End of London. Before attending Mark Lane Corn Exchange on Mondays, he called at the various baker's shops for payment. As he didn't have a bank account and because there were frequent attacks by robbers on the roads out of London, he paid the money into Strickland's account in London and collected cash from them in Dartford the next day.

Strickland's had a stand at Dartford Corn Market, which was held in the covered yard of the stage coach inn, The Royal Victoria and Bull. Merchants' stands were placed all round the walls and no stage coaches were allowed in the yard that day. It was not uncommon for seventy coaches a day to pass through Dartford, and most of them changed horses there. This created a thriving demand for oats and fodder, much of which was supplied by Stricklands.

The advent of the railways, built from the mid to late 1800s, reduced the need of fodder for the stage coach horses but happily horses were still the only form of local transport in commercial and private life.

William and James Alexander turning the home-made 40 gallon seed dressing drum.

Robert Alexander dressing seed corn with the Strickland Powder Dresser.

Mr Harold Strickland's two sons, Donald and Leslie, joined the family business in 1903 and 1909 respectively. My grandfather's trading with them was mainly selling hay from stacks in the field. Stricklands employed a man called a hay-cutter who went to the farmer's stack with his hay knife, string and hay press. He would cut out trusses of hay and weigh them out in half-hundredweights, ready for selling. The hay-cutter was employed at other times to thatch hay and corn stacks for farmers.

In later years my father did considerable business with Donald Strickland, selling him oats, wheat and barley. A certain amount of cereals was always kept back and used as homegrown seed. Cereals were, however, prone to two particular seed-borne fungus diseases—loose smut and bunt. They affected the grains and reduced crop yields; wheat in particular became unsuitable for milling. During the 1930s a powder dressing called Ceresan came on to the market, which when applied to the seed at sowing time very much reduced the incidence of these fungus diseases. In order to coat the seed with the powder dressing my father made a seed dressing 'apparatus' which consisted of a 40-gallon drum mounted on a frame and rotated by two men. This mixed 4 ounces of dressing powder with two bushels of seed grain.

This seed dressing method was, however, not practical for treating the large quantities of seed sold by merchants. Mr Leslie Strickland, being very mechanically minded, invented and subsequently marketed a Powder Dressing Machine which was driven by either an electric motor or by belt drive from other machinery in a merchant's warehouse. He built the prototype machine in the workshop of his garage and, after perfecting it, he marketed the Strickland Powder Dresser in 1934 which was sold for £34. The last Dresser to be built was number 489 in 1966. We purchased a Strickland Dresser in 1950 for our newly built grain store where provision had been made to feed cleaned seed into it from an overhead grain bin. The dresser, which has been used for over forty years, continues to give satisfactory results. But we have not let cobwebs grow over the home-made 40-gallon drum dresser: it was only semi-retired and is occasionally used to mix small batches of grass seeds.

CHAPTER 9
Castle Farm 1932

My brother, my sister and I started our first school lessons in 1928 at the tender ages of six and four. We were disciplined by Miss Woolley who had a kindergarten school at her home, Woodside in Eynsford High Street. Her father Samuel Woolley had been headmaster at the Board School Eynsford from 1874 to 1918.

From September 1930 we went by car to a small school in Otford. Betty Brown, the daughter of the haulage contractor in Eynsford, R.E.G. Brown, also went to the same school and this made up a carload of four children—an arrangement that continued all our school days, with our parents and Mr Brown having their set days to take the children to school.

One of my earliest memories of that school run was looking down to the hop gardens at Castle Farm, Shoreham, which we could see soon after going under the railway bridge at Eynsford station. In the summer of 1932, I remember my parents discussing the possibility of renting the farm. Mr Templeton, the tenant, had run into financial difficulties and was leaving. Lord Mildmay of Shoreham, the landlord, was keen to find a new tenant and made the offer to my father. The other farms in Eynsford and Farningham, which he had taken between 1922 and 1925, were ticking over quite well. He felt able to continue to expand and took the bold decision in September 1932 to rent the 312 acres of Castle Farm. There was a very large farmhouse, suitable for a farm bailiff, cottages for six families, a cowshed, loose boxes, hay barn, stables for eight horses, cart lodge, implement shed and twin oast houses, and numerous other buildings.

The farm's original name was Shoreham Castle Farm. The history of Shoreham Castle is somewhat obscure but it is believed that it was a battlement building in the early thirteenth century and that it was moated. In 1307 (King Edward II's reign) it was the home of Hugo de Poynty. Rebuilding took place around 1575 and the remains of the old castle were incorporated into the walls of the new building, a farmhouse. The Mildmay family owned Castle Farm from 1823, and the Alexander family bought it in 1948.

An old parchment map dated about 1720 shows hops being grown at Castle Farm on the same fields as they were in 1932 and indeed hops are still being grown there today, sixty years later. They require good deep soil and there is only a limited acreage close to but out of the flood level of the river Darent. My father had no previous experience of growing hops and the industry had been experiencing severe depression for several years. However, in 1932 the Hops Marketing Board was formed and it was anticipated that prices would begin to improve. Although there were only 15 acres, the hops were expected to provide a substantial income to the farm. The river meadows were ideal for livestock grazing and a herd of thirty Shorthorn cows was started.

Father and Mother taking the children on an outing in the 1932 maroon-colour Essex car.

The crops being grown on the farm were wheat, barley and oats, cabbages, savoys and broccoli. There were two three-horse teams for the field work and a pony to take the churns of milk to catch the 8 a.m. train at Eynsford station. The milk was bought by Mr Ramsdale who had a retail round and a dairy shop in Gravesend. When my father went once a month to be paid for the milk, we children used to ply him to go too, as we were each given a sixpence and some sweeties by Mr Ramsdale—a fond memory of childhood days!

The first year's hop picking in 1933 was a new venture. The majority of the hop pickers came from London docks, south of the Thames. Whole families of three generations either arrived by lorry or else we carted them down from Eynsford station. Their living accommodation was in large bell tents which had previously been used by the Army. They had a communal cookhouse in the meadow, consisting of an open fireplace with a tin roof but no sides. In 1935 a block of purpose-made hopper huts was built and there was a piped water supply. Every family or hut received one

An early 1800 painting of Castle Farm house.

bundle of firewood (called a faggot or a bavin) each day for cooking and to keep themselves warm. Some hop pickers came daily from Dartford and Eynsford and were transported in Mr Hever's buses (ex Little Mote Garage).

As hop yields increased we built more hopper huts. In 1939 we built a new Oast House of square design. Electricity was laid on to the farm in 1935 and this allowed the use of electric fans which gave a higher air speed than the old single-cylinder diesel engine could muster for drying the hops.

Hops require the eye of an experienced person during the whole of their growing season and the subsequent drying in the Oast. Growers relied very much on their hop factor for advice, and the hop factor would 'walk the hop garden' regularly with the grower and alert him to any looming disease problems. As he obtained a commission for handling and grading the grower's hops he was eager for the grower to produce a good crop. Dudley Le May was our hop factor for many years and we maintained a lifelong friendship with the family.

One of the key workers at Castle Farm was Eric Watts. He and his two brothers Ernie and Jack started work for my father in September 1925 at Bower Farm having previously worked at Lower Austin Lodge Farm for Mr. Hynard. In 1934 Eric moved to Castle Farm when he married Molly Wellard whose father was a builder in Eynsford. Eric became fully involved in the growing and drying of hops and made them his lifetime work. He always enjoyed chatting about hops to any interested person. He worked at Castle Farm for over sixty years until he retired in 1987. Eric's brother Ernie became the shepherd at Bower Farm and Jack moved to Home Farm where he looked after the dairy young stock and reared chickens and ducks for the poultry market. One of the earliest memories the Watts family had of my father was seeing him ride a BSA motorbike and sidecar and later driving a khaki-coloured Star motorcar with a 'dickie' rear seat.

Castle Farm house, 1912.

Apple orchards were planted at Castle Farm on the better soils away from the river and on rising ground high enough to escape all but the severest spring frosts during blossom time. My father had established a fruit tree nursery at Home Farm with certified root stock stool beds from East Malling Research Station. Jack Turner, his fruit tree expert, performed the budding or grafting of the variety of apple required on the planted root stock. We therefore grew all our own fruit trees. In 1936, four

Castle Farm house, 1990.

Castle Farm Shoreham

Owners/Occupiers		Tenant Farmers	
c 1300	Hugo de Poyutz (For Archbishop of Canterbury)	1841 – 1876	Samuel Love
c 1330 – *c* 1380	Roger de Chaindois	1876 – *c* 1887	William R. W. English
c 1380 – *c* 1470		*c* 1887 – *c* 1899	Cecil Leventhorpe
c 1470 – *c* 1530	John De Newburgh (Newborough?)	1913 –	Robert Wilson
c 1530 – 1575	Roger Newborough	1927 – 1932	Mathew & Duncan Templeton
1575 – 1689	Thomas Polhill	1932 – 1948	William Alexander
1689 – 1712	Paul D'Avanda (London Lawyer)		
1712 – *c* 1795	John Bovrett (London Lawyer)		
c 1795 – 1823	Sit Walter Sterling		
1823 – 1948	Humphrey St John Mildmay Lord Mildmay (Anthony)		
1948 –	The Alexander Family		

Owner – occupiers and tenants since c.1300.

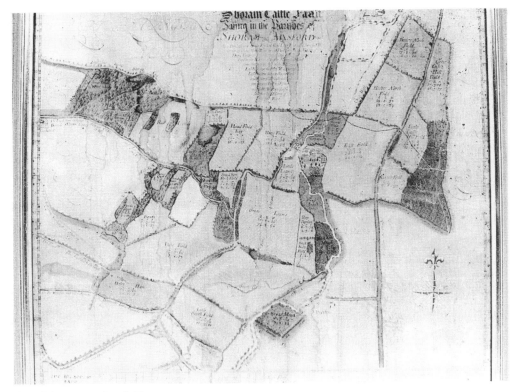

Parchment map Castle Farm, 1720.

Hop picking September 1957.

acres of Cox apple trees, with Lord Lambourne as a one-in-nine pollinator, were planted. They were on Type IX, the dwarf root stock, and were supported by horizontal wires attached to posts. The orchard performed well and was not grubbed until 1968, probably rather later than its economical lifespan.

In 1938, five acres of plums were planted. They replaced a hop garden which was grubbed the previous year as its structure was so different from our other hop gardens. Its hop rows were extra narrow at 6 foot, and the garden had Butcher wirework. This required the skill of a man on stilts to string it. Mr Willis who grew a small acreage of hops at Telston Lane in Otford used to come with his stilts to do this special stringing. Our other hop gardens had 7-foot-wide rows and were strung from the ground using a long bamboo pole which had an eye of pipe on the top end through which the string ran continuously. This method was called umbrella or Worcester work stringing.

The varieties of plum trees planted were Warwickshire Droopers, a yellow plum, and Bennets Blue. Cherry plums, rarely seen now, were planted around the perimeter of the orchard. The yellow plums became ripe during the hop-picking time and the London men and boys in the hop garden were always glad to earn more money at the plum picking than they could hope to earn at hop picking. This plum orchard was grubbed in 1963, three years after we began picking hops by machine, as the London labour was not then available.

Other apple orchards were planted in succession in 1950, 1955, 1960, 1966, 1968 and they generally had a 20–25-year lifespan. One variety of apple for which we have always commanded a good trade is Norfolk Royal. It is ready to pick a few weeks after Worcester apples and just before Coxes are ready. It ripens with a slightly waxy skin, which gives it a highly polished look. It is full of red colour and eats crisp and juicy.

Picked hops being measured.

We term it 'love at first bite'. My father grew the first three trees of Norfolk Royal in Furlongs orchard at Eynsford in 1928. The soil at the top of that sloping field was not really ideal for growing fruit trees, having an element of chalk deep down, but the variety thrived very well. A similar soil structure existed on the sloping fields above the spring frosts danger at Castle Farm, and the Norfolk Royal variety has been grown there for over forty years.

Savoys of the cabbage family with crinkled leaves were grown at Home Farm and the other farms. They were a late harvested variety cut during February and March and were particularly suited to the chalk soils as they had a long growing period in coming to maturity and could 'stand' a while when ready to cut. The commercial varieties that were available for growing were not consistently good, so my father decided to breed his own strain. This was done by careful selection of the very best heads to grow on for seed and then transplanting the head and root in a field in isolation from other brassica. The transplanted savoys produced seed that summer and this was sown the following April. It was therefore a two-year period before one was able to assess the improvement. The selection process was started in 1930 and by 1940 a very high standard of improvement, with consistently good marketable heads, had been achieved. Other varieties were compared each year with this new variety, which by 1940 was really outstanding as a late savoy. Seed merchants were invited to see the trials and they became very interested.

In 1940 Alexander's No. 1 Savoy Late Dark Green was launched. The seed was advertised each week in the *Farmers' Weekly* at 20 shillings per pound. Demand steadily increased until we were producing two tons of seed annually.

The method of selection was to mark the selected savoy with a splint stick, stuck in the ground through the leaves beside the savoy head. These splints were made

William and James selecting savoys for seed production.

primarily for holding down straw covering apples packed for the market in half-sieves. The splints were made by Mr Wood in Shoreham from young hazel wood. My father walked for days on end to and fro across the fields of savoys with a bundle of splints under one arm and scanning two rows on either side, marking the selected savoys with a splint. James and I became apprenticed on Wednesday afternoons by taking only two rows each and were trained to get our eye in for selecting the correct type. Colour, size and the fold of the leaf were dominant factors. If small heads were selected, for example, they became more pronounced in the progeny seen two years later. We had a half-day at school on Wednesdays and Saturdays and always preferred to be on the farm on those afternoons as against playing any type of school sport. The selection of savoys for seed had a high priority with us in the winter and riding on the hay carts in the summer!

The selected savoys were pulled up and bagged in tens and carted to Castle Farm for transplanting. The field was prepared in the autumn and left ridged-up, looking like potato baulks, so it always remained relatively dry for hand digging and planting. This was a labour-intensive process necessary to produce a high-quality seed. 8,000 heads were planted each year. We were seeding 8 per cent of the prime heads growing in the field whereas seed merchants were roguing out 10 per cent of the poorest heads in a field and leaving 90 per cent for seed. To assist the savoys in running to seed a cross was cut in the head with a knife early in April and this gave more uniformity for seed head emergence.

The stage at which to harvest was quite critical. It was when the seeds in the pods had turned from green to mauve but before they were black, otherwise they shattered. The seed was cut by hand and tied into a sheaf and hung up on wires under the roof of the cattle yards at Furlongs Farm. The open areas in the roof were netted over with fishermen's nets (no plastic netting at that time) to prevent the sparrows eating our 'gold dust' seed. Once the seed had finished its ripening process it was

Alexander's No. 1 Savoy Seed in 1lb and 2lb sealed bags.

threshed out with the ordinary threshing machine used for corn stacks in the field.

The seed was cleaned with special commercial seed-cleaning machinery. It had to comply with the purity and germination standards of the statutory seed regulations. Seed was marketed in half-pound, one-pound and two-pound specially printed cotton bags, tied up with string and sealed with a lead seal which made an imprint of the initials W.A.E.K. (William Alexander Eynsford, Kent). The savoy received an Award of Merit after trials at Wisley by the Royal Horticultural Society in November 1945—a rare achievement for farmer-produced seed. James and I spent many days cleaning, weighing, tying and sealing these bags of seed. We sat on an old car seat on top of a bushel apple box with a door as a table to bag up the savoy seed, with a small electric fire as a luxury to keep our fingers active enough in the cold frosty weather. The table-top was covered with barrage balloon fabric retrieved when one came down near Lullingstone Station—a railway station that was never opened. And with these basic facilities, James and I became very good at the job.

We continued marketing Alexander's No. 1 Savoy until 1972 at 42 shillings per pound when the decision to stop growing savoys was taken, for three basic reasons. First, the acreage of savoys that were being grown was decreasing as winters had generally become milder and spring greens were available earlier in the year. Secondly, deep-frozen foods were gaining popularity, peas in particular being an easier vegetable for the housewife to serve. And thirdly, the cost of hand labour had become too high a proportion of our production costs. But although we stopped growing and marketing Alexander's No. 1 Savoy in 1972, it is interesting to see that the strain is still listed in seedsmen's catalogues some twenty years later. The good name lives on.

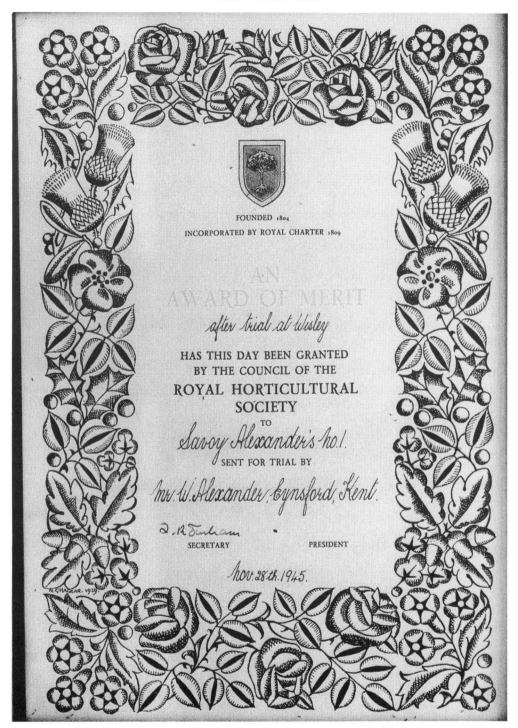

The Royal Horticultural Societies Award of Merit Certificate for Alexander's No. 1 Savoy, 1945.

CHAPTER 10
Home Farm touch and go

By the mid-1930s the depression of the earlier years had started to ease. However, at Home Farm another cloud on the horizon appeared. Both Sir William and Lady Emily Hart Dyke had died in 1931 aged ninety-three and eighty-four respectively. The payment of death duties was considerable and it was deemed necessary to sell land and properties. The Hart Dyke family sold over 5,000 acres of the Lullingstone estate, which included Home Farm, to the Kemp Town Brewery in July 1934 for £150,000. The Southern Railway was electrifying the line and the Kemp Town Brewery was speculating. It is perhaps of passing interest to note that 1934 was the year in which the speed limit of 30 miles per hour in built up areas was introduced.

During 1935 a survey of land at Hulberry, near Lullingstone, was carried out by Sir Alan Cobham, who was searching for possible suitable sites for another London airport within twenty miles radius of the capital.

The Kemp Town Brewery had discussions with the Southern Railway to ascertain its interest in purchasing some land. As a result, the Southern Railway, in August 1936, paid a deposit of £500 for the option to buy land. However, the Southern Railway eventually decided it would be too expensive to pursue the project itself so it did not take up the option which expired in 1938. It hoped that the London County Council or the Air Ministry might take up the option instead.

Southern Railway went ahead with the building of Lullingstone Station, which was completed in 1939 and ready for use in April with the stop being shown in its printed timetable. The purpose of the station was to give access to the airport site for the construction workers, and to service an anticipated housing development. A plan of the proposed airport was published in several newspapers and magazines.

Then the Second World War intervened. During the war Heathrow came into existence and it was decided in due course to extend Heathrow as the new London airport instead of Lullingstone. The whole project for the Lullingstone site was finally abandoned in 1947. The Alexander family were very relieved with the ultimate outcome as it had been very touch and go, and the construction of an airport would have completely evaporated Eynsford's charm as a village.

Nevertheless, it is worth remembering that it was the construction of the railway that has contributed through the years to Eynsford's prosperity and to its residential attractiveness. On 29 December 1858 a meeting was convened at the Crown Hotel, Sevenoaks, under the chairmanship of Lord Amherst, and the Sevenoaks Railway Company was formed. The Hart Dykes and the Mildmays, as landlords of the proposed route, were very much involved in the discussions. The route was from Swanley Junction (then called Sevenoaks Junction) to the Bat and Ball at Sevenoaks. The construction of the tunnel from Swanley was a major undertaking. It was 700

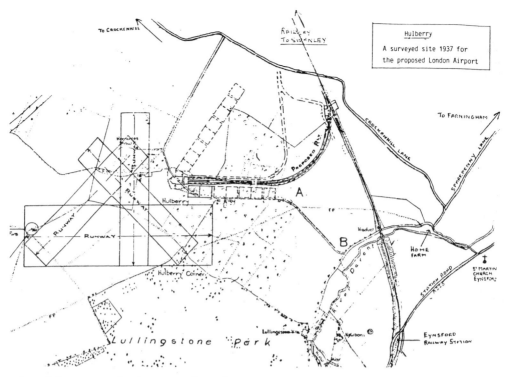

Plan of the runways for the proposed London Airport.

yards long and half a million tons of chalk were excavated. This was used to build the embankment beyond the viaduct. At the time of construction there was a tremendous building programme in London and bricks were difficult to obtain. So the bricks for this viaduct, which has nine 30-foot spans 75 feet high over the river Darent, and Lullingstone Lane were made at Eynsford in the field we still call the brickfield, which is next to the Water Works Pumping mains building. The whole construction with pick and shovel was a Herculean task and is a great tribute to those who designed and built the railway and viaduct. Many of the hundreds of workmen were housed in Eynsford and the neighbouring villages.

The railway was opened on Monday, 2 June 1862. The inaugural train stopped by the viaduct for the company directors and the privileged shareholders to admire the view (as we all do today). The train service created a need for punctuality; the church clock, however, did not possess a minute hand, so a subscription was raised to make this useful addition. In 1903 the clock was removed for repairs and repositioned higher up in the church tower. It was seventy-three years after the railway was opened that the line was electrified. The first electric train ran on Sunday, 6 January 1935. We farmers were very pleased to see fewer steam trains from then on, as the engine drivers used to stoke up their fires when they came out of the Swanley tunnel. If the wind direction was the wrong way, sparks from the train's funnel would set our corn fields alight at harvest time. Insurance claims were an annual event.

It is worthwhile noting some history about Eynsford Pumping Station, which is sited on land next to the viaduct that at one time was also part of Home Farm. The Metropolitan Water Board well was sunk in 1921. It is 12 feet in diameter and 90 feet deep, and it is lined with cast-iron segments and bricks. Mr J. W. James, the chairman

Eynsford Railway Viaduct and Metropolitan Water Board pumping station.

of the Works and Store Committee of the MWB, inaugurated this new well station at Eynsford on 23 June 1926. Subsequently there came a need for additional supplies of water and a bore-hole was sunk close by in 1941. This was 24 inches in diameter and 200 feet deep, and was commissioned for use in 1943.

Although there was great depression from the early to the mid 1930s, farmers tended to remain optimistic. My father's cousin, Jack Steven, used to say, 'Farm as if you were going to live for ever and live as if you were going to die tomorrow.' The happy medium was a more practical outlook. In 1935 the Ministry of Agriculture's Attested Herd Scheme was launched. The four dairy herds at Home Farm, New Barn Farm, Manor Farm and Castle Farm were amongst the very first to be registered 100 per cent tuberculosis-free, with the registered numbers 35, 36, 37 and 38. This was a great tribute to my father's forethought of more than twelve years earlier. The registration into the scheme meant special requirements for farm retail milk, so Home Farm premises needed some improvements. An extension was built on to the rear of Home Farm house which incorporated a white-tiled dairy for cooling and bottling the milk and an insulated chilled milk room for storage of both bottles and churns of milk.

My mother was extremely pleased with the extension which gave an enlarged living room above and another bedroom higher up. The 'evacuation' from the scullery of the dairy was a boon, especially for Mondays—washing day. Monday mornings at Home Farm had a strict ritual as far back as I can remember. The first job, at 7 o'clock, was for one of the farm men to check the water, oil, petrol (supplied in 2-gallon Pratts petrol cans) and the tyre pressure of all the cars and vans. Then up went the clothes drying lines ready for my mother to peg out her washing. Woe betide anyone who left a vehicle the wrong side of the washing line and wanted it out. That was the easiest way to start the week wrong. The maid would do the ironing in the afternoon whilst mother attended to the farm book work, which involved entering the weekly milk weighing records of every cow's milk, any calving dates, service or AI details. All heifer calves had their black and white markings sketched on cards which were then sent for entry into the *Friesian Herd Book*. Also, it was a statutory requirement to record animal movements. Other desk work included answering letters—always hand written—paying accounts and sending invoices, particularly for Savoy Seed sales. The correspondence for booking hop pickers' huts started in March and continued until the picking began at the end of August. My mother's book-keeping was meticulous. In due course James and I became more involved but it was not until January 1974 that we employed our first farm secretary, Jean Mayoss, and then invested in a typewriter. Gran, as our mother was by then called, had been at her desk for fifty-five years. Decimalization, PAYE and NIC were some of the major changes during that time.

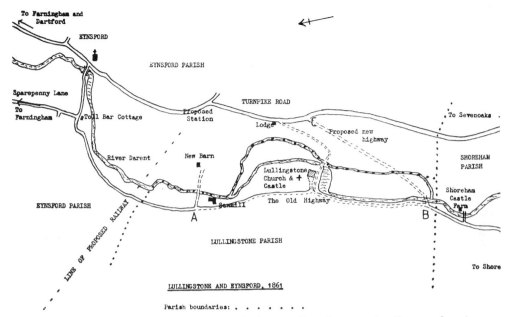

1861 plan of Lullingstone and Eynsford roads showing line of proposed railway and station.

The increase in cattle numbers, again in the mid-1930s, meant that more and better winter housing for the young stock and in-calf heifers was needed. A new cattle yard, 90 feet by 40 feet, was built at Castle Farm in 1936, and, in the same year, one at Furlongs Farm, 60 feet by 60 feet, on land that we owned. This one was home-constructed and had one-ninth open centre and eight-ninths covered with corrugated iron sheets. It was completely windproof and had the feeding racks and troughs on the perimeter. It is just as sound fifty-six years later, with the same sliding door continuing to slide so easily. This yard was used for hanging up the sheaves of savoy seed to finish their ripening and so the cattle yard had a concrete floor from which the shattered seed could be swept up. This yard was so successful that another double one, 60 feet by 90 feet, was built in 1938.

James and I had always been concreting enthusiasts and Father was pleased when concreting had been laid but not keen on spending the money to do so. When he went away to Scotland for a week's visiting, therefore, we would prepare an area of a yard, a road or a shed, and concrete it before he came back. It was too late then to complain about the costs and as we always made a good job, he was usually pleased. Our first experience of concreting was on a dirt floor in a rather Heath Robinson tool shed and we made a real *faux pas*. We mixed three parts sand and one part cement, which was correct, but we used builder's sand instead of washed sand. The floor never went really hard with using builder's (soft) sand—so we learnt that lesson by our own mistake. We have been able ever since to give advice to people about the correct sand to use for different jobs.

Improvements to buildings and/or the construction of new ones was, in my father's view, as important an aspect of good farming as was keeping the land in good heart with husbandry techniques. James and I therefore had a very sound grounding in the design and construction of farm buildings from a father whose ideas were so practical. The construction of new buildings was, however, severely restricted in 1939 because of the war. Every effort had to go to repairing bomb-damaged buildings.

CHAPTER 11

Wartime farming

The declaration of war on Sunday, 3 September 1939 brought an impetus to the production of home-produced foods. The country's self-sufficiency was increased from under 50 per cent to nearly 75 per cent during the war. A government scheme had been established by the end of 1936 for increased food production should the need arise, and Agricultural Executive Committees were formed in every county and known as War Ags. Their plans were put into effect in August 1939. Lord Cornwallis was chairman of the Kent War Ag. Each district had its own representative. William Alexander of Eynsford and John Dinnis of Shoreham were key men. Farmers were ordered to plough up a percentage of their grass fields to grow wheat and barley. Land which had been idle for years was ploughed to produce food. Lullingstone Park, overrun with rabbits and deer, was ploughed by the War Ag. The nine-hole golf course on the lower side of Sparepenny Lane was ploughed. It belonged to the six founder members. The steep fields along the top side of Sparepenny Lane, uncultivated for many years, were also ploughed. These are just some local recognizable examples. During the war years, 1939 to 1945, the grass acreage in Kent was reduced from 390,000 acres to 220,000 acres, while the arable acreage increased from 250,000 to 430,000 acres. 'Dig for Victory' was a war slogan, and allotments were brought back into cultivation.

The Women's Land Army contributed greatly to the labour force for the production of food. Born on 1 July 1939, the WLA received hundreds of applications every day. The Land Girls were drafted to the farms where they were most needed and were taught the various skills from milking cows to driving tractors. Kent had the highest number of Land Girls in any county in spite of the fact that Kent was in the front line of defence during the war and was far from being a safe county in which to work. The record number of Land Girls in Kent was 3,968 in 1944.

Mechanization of farming had a real boost. The number of horses began to decline, slowly at first but soon the decrease accelerated. The number of horses on farms in Kent reduced from 8,500 in 1939 to under 4,000 ten years later whilst tractors increased from less than 3,000 to over 10,000. A pair of horses could plough one acre per day; a tractor, with a 2-furrow plough three acres per day.

Everyone during the war put maximum effort into the production of food, using all the daylight hours given. The harvests in 1940 and 1941 were fortunately good years, which were literally a godsend.

Many school classrooms had their own allotments. It was well recognized that the best plot at Dartford Grammar School was the one belonging to form VIa of which I was a pupil. I dug, fertilized and hoed the ground at the right time, true farmer fashion, and therefore grew the best vegetables.

During the early days of the war especially, one could not envisage what future

Ploughing up the centuries-old Lullingstone Park watched by the Kent War Agricultural committee members.

events might take place. Eynsford was on the direct route for bombing London, and we made a deep dug-out in the garden at the back of the house, in which we slept every night for over a year. Bombing was severe and all the farms in Farningham, Eynsford and Shoreham suffered considerable damage from high explosives, incendiary bombs, V1 doodlebugs and V2 rockets.

Sunday, 15 September 1940 was one of the most memorable days. It was the climax of the Battle of Britain and it was said that over one thousand German aircraft were sent against London that day. Air-raid sirens regularly sounded Warnings and All Clears. We always carried our gas masks with us. One of the air-raid warnings given that day was just before midday, and we learnt that a German twin-engined Dornier bomber had been shot down at Castle Farm. It landed in a field just above the hop huts which were buzzing with hop pickers, it being a Sunday. We all went down after lunch to have a look but were barred entrance to the field which was by then guarded by soldiers. Just then there was another siren warning and soon after we heard the very familiar sound of bombs whistling down and exploding. They were in the direction of Eynsford so we hurried back to Home Farm, only to see the thatched roof of the old barn burning fiercely. It had received a direct hit. The fire engine was there and a large crowd of people had gathered. Fortunately no one was hurt, but a valuable bull in a pen close by had been injured by shrapnel and had to be shot. All that remained after the fire was extinguished were the charred and burnt timbers and the flint and brick walls.

Ten days later, on 25 September, another stick of bombs fell in nearly the same line. One bomb demolished six houses in Riverside by the Plough pub, a second bomb

German Dornier 17Z bomber which crash-landed at Castle Farm 15 September 1940.

landed in the road by the entrance into Home Farm and a third bomb in the footpath field towards the railway. The bomb by Home Farm made only a small crater which was immediately filled in for traffic to use the road. But at 4.30 the next morning, we were awakened in our dug-out by a huge explosion. This was from the bomb in the road which was a delayed-action bomb—a type of bomb hitherto unknown. It had penetrated quite deeply and on its second explosion it destroyed the gas, electricity, water and sewer services. The walls of the old barn were blown down too and the farmyard was completely covered with stones and soil. I remember having to sweep a pathway from the house across to the cowshed so that the milk churn carrier could be wheeled there. The milking had to continue as usual, by the light of a Tilley lamp and storm lanterns. Later that morning I found a piece of shrapnel which was just small enough for me to post through the front door letter box. My mother was not at all pleased with me when she found that I was the culprit—when it dropped it cut a hole in the linoleum of the hall floor. There was a third line of bombs dropped which again jumped Home Farm house. They were small bombs and fell in the soft ground of the meadows.

It is an eerie sound, that of bombs whistling down, and one evening whilst playing cards we heard them. Every explosion seemed to be nearer, so we all crouched under tables and desks. That stick of bombs fell in the meadows behind Eynsford Paper Mills and six of our in-calf heifers were killed that night.

We had a total of about 150 high-explosive bombs, several hundred incendiaries, 6 V1s and one V2 rocket (launched in Holland), which landed on our farms but fortunately with no human casualties.

Our acreage of corn had increased considerably during the war and extra labour was needed, especially at harvest time. The corn was cut by a binder pulled by a pair of horses and the sheaves were stacked up in eights or tens to keep them dry. Land Girls and older schoolchildren were invaluable in this area and they also helped with the carting and stack-building. It was all hand work pitching the sheaves onto the carts and off again onto the stacks. Some wheat was always threshed straight from the field at harvest time to obtain straw for thatching the corn stacks. Thatching is a very skilled

Burnt-down thatched barn at Home Farm after two direct hits with bombs 15th and 25th September, 1940.

job and a most satisfying art that I enjoyed learning. Two skilled persons could thatch a stack in one day. The straw had to be laid out, wetted with buckets of water, and pulled out into the number of bundles required for the length of the stack roof. Splints and string across the stack secured the thatch. The bottom layer straw was clipped at eaves level for neatness.

An unusual crop that was grown only during the war was flax. It is of the same family as the linseed grown today for linseed oil, but flax was much taller as it was grown for the fibre in the stem. For harvesting, it was pulled up out of the ground and not cut like corn. Flax pullers made in Belgium were used and the sheaves went to the flax factory at Pluckley near Ashford where it was retted. The strong fibres were used for making coarse linen, ropes and canvas.

Hop picking, apple picking and potato lifting were other labour-intensive jobs that followed harvesting. We employed a regular staff of 40 men and boys, plus casuals for the seasonal work. Four Land Girls worked on the farms. Connie Haynes was from Eynsford, Nora Heddle was from Dartford, while Pat Wood came from Woolwich and Joan Elkins from London. They had all volunteered for the Land Army and had a period of training. Their most regular jobs included hand-milking the cows, feeding calves and young stock. They helped the men with some of the lighter jobs, the men being very happy to have them work with them. We remember how fond the Land Girls were of looking after two particular bulls, Ongar Setske Bertus and Royal Hilkeejan. They would feed the bulls and secure them by a rope through the ring on their nose or with a halter while they mucked out the pen.

Land Girls carting dung and spreading it.

The 21-year lease of Bower Farm, Eynsford, expired in September 1943 and, as my father was unable during the preceding year to negotiate a new rent acceptable to him with the landlords, the farm was given up on that date. In 1942 Dunstall Farm, Shoreham, on Lord Dunsany's estate was on the market for a new tenant. There were 242 acres, 40 acres of chalk land just beyond Shoreham station and 202 acres at the top of the hill off Fackenden Lane. My brother and I walked the fields with our father to survey the land. The fields were in a dilapidated state, many of them having ant hills and also small shrubs growing. My father always had a five-foot-long stick with him. This was used for various purposes: to make a cow stand up in its stall in the cowshed; to point with; to lean on; to measure, as it had a ring marked every foot up the stick, and, on this occasion to prod into the ground. The prodding indicated that the soil was very stony—a truer word was never spoken about Dunstall Farm. I suppose the challge of improving a farm made him take the decision to rent it and the tenancy started from September 1942.

James and I worked alternate weeks at Dunstall, ploughing the fields using a Caterpillar D2 tractor. It was a very cold winter, the ground was stony and many of the fields were steep. The experience taught us how to set a plough and to be tough. There were no tractor cabs in those early days. The fields were drilled with spring wheat and the first year's crops were not very good but at least it was additional food for the country. After threshing the stacks of corn there was a lot of straw available, so my father designed and built an Alexander Straw Yard. The walls were 15 feet high and constructed with hop garden poles laced across with horizontal wires at 12-inch intervals on both sides of the pole and filled in between with combed straw. The yard had an open roof but the cattle were adequately sheltered from which ever way the wind was blowing. The yard used masses of straw, this being the purpose for which it was designed. During the spring of 1943 the cows and calves were transferred from Bower Farm to Dunstall Farm and George Pavitt, who reared the calves, moved there too. In 1950 we changed the calf-rearing procedure of feeding them cow's milk to feeding gruel (milk powder). And so ended a period of nearly fifty years of hand-milking a few cows specially to rear calves.

On one night in January 1944 the German Luftwaffe dropped an estimated 16,000 incendiary bombs in the valley and on the hills around Shoreham. The sky was ablaze.

The Women's Land Army girls riddling potatoes.

Dunstall Farm received several hundred incendiaries, some of which set the straw yard walls alight and burnt them out. The cattle escaped into the fields. A mile away towards Eynsford there was a collection of buildings and a house in which a family of ten Irish people lived. It was called Preston Hill Farm. A land mine which came down by parachute landed on the farmstead and killed Mrs McCaughan and two of her children. The house and buildings were no more. This land was most inaccessible from the bottom road and it joined on to Dunstall's furthest field so my father began farming this 40 acres too. The land belonged to the Kent County Council. Dunstall and Preston Hill farms had eight high-explosive bomb craters in their fields.

In the spring later that year there was a sudden influx of Royal Air Force men and vehicles into the area and they came complete with their own bulldozers. We were informed that they had come to prepare sites for barrage balloons. The sky was soon filled with these silver-coloured monsters which were held down (or up) with steel wire cables. On 14 June 1944, the Germans began launching their unmanned VI flying bombs, known as doodlebugs. They were sent from France towards London at over 100 per day. Their engines emitted a very loud throbbing noise, and they were low flying and could easily be seen from the ground. It was only when the engine cut out that one was in real danger, as at that moment they dived to the ground and exploded. At night they were easily visible as their engine exhausts gave out a long flame. We had stopped sleeping down in the dug-out by that time, so when we heard a doodlebug's loud throbbing noise during the night, we would jump out of bed to watch it in the sky. One just had to live with their potential danger. Statistics show that by 7 July 2,754 VIs had been launched, and by 10 September the total was over 8,000. The ack-ack guns along the south-east coast shot down a large percentage into the sea, and fighter planes accounted for many more. The barrage balloons were the last defence for London. There were just under 2,000 of them strategically placed.

Six doodlebugs came down on our farms. On hitting the ground, their explosion scattered shrapnel and short lengths of steel wire. The explosion made only a small crater. Several cattle were killed by the shrapnel and others picked up the two- to four-inch lengths of steel wire when grazing or, in the winter, from eating the hay baled in these fields. A piece of wire or metal in an animal's stomach would make it ill.

Straw-walled cattled yard, Dunstall Farm, 1943.

We used a mine detector to indicate if there was a foreign body in the stomach. An operation to extract the wire saved the animals from dying. The veterinary surgeon gave the animal a local anaesthetic, made an incision and very soon became masterly in extracting steel wire. After the wound was stitched up, the animal was soon happily chewing its cud once again.

The RAF men manning the barrage balloons sites—of which there were seven on the farms—often had some spare time during their 'off' periods and they were willing to help with farm work which was close by their quarters. Farm mechanization had not made much progress in many spheres at that time. There was always hand hoeing of cabbage and savoy plants to be done in July and August; and work in the corn fields during August and September.

Some forty-five years later, it seems quite unbelievable how much labour was needed to produce brassicas. In April we sowed the cabbage and savoy seed with a one- or two-row seed drill which was pulled by one man while another walked behind, steering the drill. The seed rows were 12 inches apart and on the return sowing down the seed bed, the previously drilled row was firmed in by a barrow wheel. The seedlings emerged in about ten days and it was most important to keep an eye out for the flea beetle which could devastate the plant in a day during hot sunny weather. If there were beetles about, the plant bed would be dusted with hessian sandbags partly filled with derris dust which we would shake as we walked up and down the field. We made marvellous progress in later years by using a 10-foot-wide hand-pushed grass-seed shandy barrow to apply the dust. The plant bed was on fairly poor soil, which grew nice strong woody plants that, when planted out in the fields, rooted far better than the long lanky ones grown on richer soils. Our field was, however, quite

Sowing savoy seed with a two-row seed drill.

stony and in order to make the hand-hoeing of the three-acre plant bed a little easier, the stones were hand-raked into rows in parts of the fields and used to repair potholes and tracks on farm roads. This helped the hoeing and helped the road, and so was considered good dual-purpose thinking. The three acres of 12-inch rows were hand hoed twice to keep them reasonably weed free (no chemical weed-control used!), and plant pulling usually started in the third week of June. One could readily pull 1,000 plants per hour. They were boxed up in bushel apple boxes and taken to the field for planting. An experienced man with a good dibber could plant 400 plants per hour—yes, 400 every hour, once one had overcome backache. We planted about 60 acres each year with a density of 8,00 plants per acre. The carefully cultivated fields were left with a light flat roll finish and had the planting rows marked out. A light frame with narrow tines spaced at 2 feet 4 inches was pulled by a horse to and fro across the field and this made tine mark rows. The field was then cross-marked so that plant spacing could be accurate.

When there had been a very dry period prior to planting, many farms would wait for rain; we, however, overcame the problem by carting water from the river to the fields. Each cross mark in the row for planting was given one tea mug of water. This wetted the soil sufficiently for planting and gave the plants' rooting system a good start. Every field was destined to produce a good crop in a dry or a wet year. Inter-row cultivation was done by a horse pulling a Garrett brake, and a few years later by a MG2 track-laying tractor of miniature size cultivating two rows at a time. Hand-hoeing was done in the plant row to keep it weed free. The barrage balloon boys were most helpful and ever so welcome.

By 1943 the number of animals on the farms had increased beyond the capacity of the buildings, and the first of the farm home sales was held in December of that year. There were thirty-five in-calf Friesian heifers catalogued. As it was our first home sale every effort was made to present the cattle in very attractive condition. We had no

Plant pulling July, 1962.

experience of this and Willie McKendric, from whom we had bought many stock bulls, volunteered to come down from Scotland and teach us the art, he being a very experienced cattle showman. Every animal was carefully clipped to make it look its best—the ears, head, along the back, the tail and tail head. Then they were ready for a shampoo and rinse, for which churnfuls of warm water were sent down to the shed from Home Farm scullery. Lastly, the heifers' horns were filed and polished—they had horns in those days, and good horns could add lots of character to an animal.

The sale was held in the new cattle yards at Furlongs Farm where each animal was chained up beside a feed trough. They were well and truly littered down knee-deep in bright straw. The cattle sale ring was constructed in timber and made sectional for use again at later sales. Straw bales for seats were placed around the ring, with farm trailers behind them and apple boxes on them for sitting on. Some prospective buyers came the evening before the sale to have a quiet look-round the heifers, while most people came an hour or so before the sale started. A hand bell was rung announcing the start of the sale, people took their seats, and the auctioneer, Mr Harry Hobson, spent about five minutes making introductory remarks to highlight the virtues of the Eynsford herd and of Mr William Alexander's farming abilities and achievements. Meanwhile, Lot 1 heifer was slowly walking round and round in the sale ring, attended by Jack Watts. It was he who for many years looked after all the heifers during their winter housing at Furlongs Farm, so it was quite right that he should have the élite position, in the ring gently encouraging the animal to walk round. He was smartly dressed and wearing a white coat and highly polished leather gaiters. His old farm cap had been replaced by a new one for that day. The vendor/breeder is always anxious, wondering how the sale will go. Lot 1 sold at 95 guineas and we did not enthuse; however, Lot 2 saw the auctioneer's hammer fall at 310 guineas and this set a good tone for the sale, which finished with the excellent average of £287. The top bid of 480 guineas was for a calved heifer and the heifer calf at foot sold for 160

First home sale of in-calf heifers at Furlongs Farm cattle yards 1st December 1943.

guineas. Pedigree cattle were always sold in guineas, the vendor receiving the pounds and the auctioneers retaining the shillings. The hustle and bustle with weeks of preparation were well and truly rewarded and my father was extremely satisfied.

Another good 'crop' of heifers were due to calve the next autumn. There would again be a number in excess of culling requirements. In this instance it was decided to modernize the cowshed at Castle Farm. The practical way to achieve this was to sell all the cows in the spring and to start with a new herd of heifers in the autumn, so a sale took place in April. A local auctioneer arranged the sale of the nineteen Friesian cows, which averaged £92, and the twelve Shorthorn cows, which averaged £26. What a difference from the all heifer sale in December.

The modernization of the cowshed included improvements to the stall positions, solid walls to replace pipe work, feeding troughs, a dunging passage and the centre pathway. Also floor levels and drainage falls were made more positive. During visits to Scotland, my father on several occasions met Mr Tommy Samuel who was the Sanitary Inspector of dairy premises in Ayrshire. He was very keen on recommending an 'uncomfortable slope' being incorporated in the grip in a byre. This wedge-shaped slope started at a height of three inches high and tapered to zero in ten inches. The cement was laid in the gutter next to each cow's stall and it discouraged her from standing back off her stall into the dung passage. This idea was incorporated in the work at the Castle Farm cowshed and proved most successful; eventually, all the cowsheds had one.

The Castle Farm sale saw the last of the Shorthorn cows leaving the Eynsford herds. They had been in the majority until about 1936, after which their numbers kept dwindling. At a Friesian Society's Members' meeting in Reading my father had told the audience, 'Those who had the miserable job of trying to sell Friesian milk in the twenties will understand what I mean about quantity being apt to block out quality. I may say I was properly sworn at by a milk buyer for keeping those wretched black and

The uncomfortable slope in the cowshed dunging passage at Manor Farm.

white "water pumps". As a result of that, fifty per cent of another breed was kept as a compromise, and after a considerable number of years of intelligent breeding, the milk of the whole herd was analysed, when it was found that the "props" were producing a lower fat content than the Friesians!'

From the late 1920s the bulls used were bred from females with consistently high butterfat pedigrees. The herd averages before the war when the cows were mainly Shorthorns seldom exceeded 750 gallons. During the war years the supply of protein foods was very limited and yields suffered. When the number of Friesians increased after the war, the yields reached the 1,000 gallons average at 3.7 per cent butterfat. By 1957 the yields averaged 1,215 gallons at 4.07 per cent BF. It was no wonder that in the Friesian circles my father was known as the Butterfat King.

Our herds peaked their yields in 1968 when 117 cows averaged 1,349 gallons at 4.05 per cent BF with a calving index of 395 days. They were cowshed milked. After 1972, the herds were amalgamated into one unit and milked in a parlour by one herdsman. They even improved their performance to average (over 100 cows) 1,368 gallons (6,206 kg) at 4.18 per cent BF with a calving index of 379 days. How times have changed. It is difficult to realize that we were still hand milking when the war ended and that it was not until 1947 that the first milking machine plant, a 'Wallace' was installed at Manor Farm. New skills had to be learnt.

Tractors were beginning to be used on farms before the war, the most common being the spade-lug wheeled Fordson. Their heavy weight and iron wheels tended to consolidate the ground, and farmers were not initially fully aware of the damage they caused to soil structure. When track-laying tractors were available one of their selling points was their lightness of soil compaction coupled with the minimum of 'wheel slip'. In 1937 we had a Caterpillar 22 petrol/paraffin track-layer, and the first diesel engine

John Deere AN tractor and Suntyne corn drill, 1957. David Clark (tractor) Steve Ledner (drill)
James, William and young William.

tractor to be bought was the ever popular Caterpillar D2 which was started by its own
petrol donkey engine. In 1939 this cost £626, which seemed a great deal of money. It
was, however ideal, for ploughing and cultivating the previously derelict fields that
were being brought back into production during the war. Its ample pulling power and
track grips were essential on the steep hilly fields on our farms. It was so successful
that my father bought two more D2s in 1941 and 1942.

The first rubber-tyred tractor to come on the farm was a John Deere, model BO,
imported from America in 1940 at a cost of £300. Initially its prime use was carting
produce, for which horses had previously been used. The horse waggons, with their
iron-tyred wooden spoke wheels were not suitable for tractors. Mr Jimmy Lambourne, the wheelwright at White Post Hill, Farningham, made the first rubber-tyred
farm trailer, with hinged sides and removable hay ladders, and what a joy it was to use.
Three more John Deere tractors were purchased during the following four years and
also three more trailers—each painted a different colour so that the removable
parts—sides, ladders, etc.—were easily identified as to which trailer they belonged.

The rubber-tyred John Deere tractors were much more versatile than the spade-lug
Fordsons. Their tyres made much less impact on the soil and they were more mobile
on the roads. They had petrol/paraffin two-cylinder engines which were started on
half-compression by turning a flywheel. Once started, they gave a toot-toot-toot
sound, so distinct from the purring sound of a four-cylinder engine. Horse-drawn
machines, when suitable, were converted for tractors to pull. Two examples being the
grass-mower and the binder. The tractor driver would then be in front of his machine

and had to turn round to see how it was working, whereas the horseman had always walked behind and could see exactly what was happening. I particularly remember one instance of teaching a new recruit to drive a tractor. After the tuition was finished his first job was very simple: to harrow a field by going round and round. He seemed quite oblivious, however, of the need to look behind occasionally to make sure that the harrows were doing a good job. He did not realize that they had become unhitched until he nearly ran over them on the next time round the field.

There is always an element of nostalgia when thinking back to some of the events when horses were being used. As schoolboys, my brother James and I used to delight in riding on the empty horse-drawn hay waggons along Lullingstone Lane when hay was being carted from Hulberry Farm to be stacked by Meadow View or at Home Farm. The cops of hay in the field were hand pitched onto the waggon and the horses moved forward from hay cop to hay cop almost by instinct. The road down from Hulberry was steep and the braking method for a horse-drawn waggon was to put a cast-iron skid-pan under one rear wheel, so the wheel on it slid down the hill. The skid-pans eventually wore out and new ones were cast in Gibson's iron foundry in Eynsford. When the hay or corn sheaves were just the other side of the railway near the Swanley tunnel, the horses and waggon used to come across the railway line. There was a gated farm level-crossing. Before you crossed you had to look carefully at the up and down lines to make sure there was no steam train on its way. When the electric trains started one had to be even more alert. In those schooldays there seemed to be long periods of sunny haymaking weather. It was certainly the rule rather than the exception and we were keen to hurry home from school to ride on the hay carts—homework or no homework. Our right to use the level-crossing was not given up until May 1974.

CHAPTER 12
Post war progress

The end of the war did not in any way signify a relaxation of the efforts to produce the maximum amount of home-grown foods, and food ration books continued to be issued up until 1953-54. However, iron and steel could now be used to manufacture goods other than war weapons. Our first major investment after the end of the war was the purchase of an ICI/Mark III Grass Drier and a new building in which to house it. Part of the orchard planted in 1922 at Furlongs Farm was grubbed as it was the most serviceable location on our land. The drier was fired by coke and later converted to gas oil. It consisted of two very large perforated tray areas which gave a batch system of drying for the fresh-cut grass and lucerne. The dried material had a very high analysis, rich in nutrients, compared with conventional haymaking, and the cows responded with higher milk yields and improved butterfat content. A lot of hand labour was involved in stoking, drying and baling the finished product with a hand-fed Nicholson baler. The grass drier was used for ten years until 1956, by which time imported foods had become more available, and labour and fuel had become too high a percentage of the total costs.

Another method of conserving the valuable nutrients of green fodder was by making silage, and this received a great deal of promotion by the agricultural Advisory Services of the government. Mr A. J. Hosier, a Wiltshire farmer, invented a wheel-driven green crop loader. This was pulled by a tractor and had a trailer attached behind, the grass being stacked on it by a man. The loader was certainly a very popular machine. The silage was made in round silos or above ground clamps. Sisalcraft paper was used to make airtight seals—this was long before plastic sheets became available. Clamps were sealed over with three to four inches of soil.

The invention at a later date of the buckrake by Rex Patterson gave a tremendous boost to silage making. Its use was only possible with the introduction of the three-point hydraulic linkage system of the Ferguson tractor. Silage pits and clamps were made in the fields in which the grass was being grown. The buckrake attached to the rear of the tractor was reversed along the mown grass sward until it was fully loaded. The tractor hydraulics lifted it clear of the ground and off it went at high speed to the clamp. The first time hand labour was used was to level the grass. The buckrake system could be considered as the forerunner of today's extensive material handling systems. We will always be grateful to Rex Patterson for his practical invention.

The Ferguson tractor's three-point hydraulic system was another milestone in mechanical invention for the farmer. The depth control system with its advantage of lifting the implement for turning in a field or for transport was a tremendous advancement as against trailing the implement behind the tractors. For this we owe our thanks and gratitude to the pioneering work of Harry Ferguson.

1948 Ferguson tractor model TE20

Harry Ferguson was born in Ireland in 1884, the son of a farmer, and one of three daughters and seven sons. His engineering brain was initially directed towards making and flying aeroplanes. His father used horses on the farm and in no way was Harry interested in horses. He spent many years developing both a tractor and a plough as these were basic for practically all farms; he was primarily concerned with the small acreage farmer. It was not until 1933 that his prototype tractor, with a two-furrow plough, was launched with its hydraulic draft control system. The first field tests, however, were very disappointing, mainly due to the hydraulic oil being heated and aerated which caused the depth control system to go haywire. Further developments took place and Harry Ferguson subsequently made a manufacturing agreement with David Brown in the UK, and between 1936 and 1939, 1,200 tractors were manufactured. Regrettably, however, they had a disagreement with each other and manufacture stopped. Meanwhile Harry Ferguson had been having discussions in America with Henry Ford, who had become enthusiastic about the Ferguson tractor and its system. A demonstration was arranged in Mrs Ford's nursery garden at Dearborn, Illinois, and comparison was made with an Allis Chalmers model B tractor and a Fordson. The Ferguson's superiority was outstanding. Henry and Harry discussed production arrangements and the responsibilities each of them would assume. They stood up, shook hands warmly and decided that the agreement was one of confidence and trust between gentlemen. This famous 'handshake agreement', as it has since become known, was almost certainly unique in the world of big business. There was never a scratch of pen or pencil to record it at the time. The first production tractors were ready by 12 June 1939 and the public launching on 29 June took place before 500 people from thirty American states and eighteen foreign countries. One of the outstanding paragraphs from the brochure describing the event read:

This is a memorable day, for we are privileged to introduce the most far-reaching series of developments in the long history of agriculture—a new system of farm mechanization consisting of a phenomenally light-weight Ford tractor of unique design incorporating the Ferguson System of hydraulic control for a line of light-weight indestructible implements.

The uptake of tractors in the months following this launch was not as great as predicted. The farmers with small acreages for whom the system was designed would not be able to use their existing trailed implements and many of them could not afford to re-equip with a new plough, cultivator etc.

In May 1940 a further demonstration took place in England with a view to the Fordson already produced in England being replaced by this new Ford/Ferguson. The war production commitments, however, ruled out this changeover and, not surprisingly, Fords in England showed no enthusiasm.

Nevertheless, just four years later many Ford/Ferguson tractors with their implements were being shipped to England under the American lease-lend scheme. They performed beautifully despite their miniature size in contrast with their big brothers. Their performance was the best advertisement that Harry Ferguson could have had. He realized that he would have to wait for the right moment to begin manufacturing under his own name in England.

That moment came just after VE day, 8 May 1945. He came to Britain and found idle buildings where war equipment had been made. A government-backed scheme was arranged and agreed between Harry Ferguson and Sir John Black of the Standard Motor Company for the manufacture at the Banner Lane Factory of Ferguson tractors and implements. The first of many hundreds of thousands of Ferguson System tractors rolled off their production line in 1946. This was the famous TE20 model with 23 hp.

The rubber-tyred tractor brought further mechanization to haymaking, including a hay sweep attached to the front of the tractor. This gathered up the hay cops or swarths on its way to the stack in the field. Manoeuvrability, however, was very restricted by the rigid attachment so my father designed a coupling with a single drawbar pin which allowed complete flexibility of steering. James and I were often asked to give field demonstrations of this improvement to interested farmers. I made a one-eighth scale model of the hay sweep—this was a good exercise in handcraft, and one I delighted in doing.

Hay elevators at the stacks in the field greatly reduced the efforts of hand-forking the hay onto the stacks; we bought Carters 'Unique' elevators at £154 for each farm. They had a reach of 33 feet and were driven by a 1-hp Lister water-cooled petrol engine (£32), many of which are now seen working in the Vintage section at Agricultural Shows.

During the winter the hay in these stacks was cut out by hand with a large cranked handle hay-knife and tied up, with two plaited coin-yarn strings, in trusses weighing about 56 pounds. A very sharp knife was essential for easy cutting, and the man doing it really cursed the presence of stones brought in from the field by that new invention, the hay sweep.

A tractor-drawn pick-up baler was the next development. We purchased, through the American lease-lend scheme, a Case baler Model NCM, engine-driven and with a 14- by 18-inch bale chamber. This was in June 1945 at a cost of £360. It was on pneumatic tyres, which we thought tremendous. It picked up the hay directly from the windrowed swarth and rammed it into the bale chamber. The tying was manual,

Sweeping cops of hay to the stack at Home Farm, June 1945.

with one person sitting each side of the bale chamber and threading a pre-cut length of wire through the bale to the other side. We worked very hard to achieve an output of 40 bales per hour. This baler was in due course superseded by an International Harvester Company baler model 50T, again engine-driven, which had needle and knotter tying with sisal string. The 1990 balers of similar size are Power Take Off (PTO) driven from the tractor and have outputs in excess of 300 bales per hour. Very large balers are also now available, forty-five years on, costing £40,000 to £50,000, which produce half a ton bales that are easily handled mechanically and are economical for transporting long distances by road. One wonders what will be the next major development.

Although combine harvesters were being used on an increasing number of farms soon after the war, it was not until 1948 that we bought our first one: the steam engine and thresher were still very much in vogue on our farms. In the district, Bruce Dollings was the local threshing contractor and his yard was just behind the houses of Fern Bank up Priory Lane in Eynsford. Before buying a rubber-tyred John Deere Model D tractor with a cable winch, he used his large steam engine to move and drive the thresher. Each day, by horse and cart, we took 10 hundredweight of coal and 100 gallons of water for the steam engine. The driver needed to light the boiler at 5.30 a.m. in order to have steam up by 7 a.m., ready to start threshing.

Every year, thirty to forty days were spent threshing, and it required a large team of workers. Land Girls were used when available, and from 1945, German prisoners of war were employed too. The POWs were paid 1 shilling an hour and Land Girls 1s. 5d. Although in todays terms this seems little money, it was the going rate at that time. Full-time farm employees were paid £3 10s. for a 48-hour week and had six days' paid holiday plus six bank holidays. The threshing team consisted of three persons on the corn stack, two on the thresher (the feeder man cut the sheaf string before feeding it into the threshing drum), and one man bagging off the corn into

Bruce Dollings threshing corn stack 1936 at Farningham.

hired four-bushel Starkey Room sacks (which held 2¼ cwts wheat, 2 cwts barley, or 1½ cwts oats). Our local sack depot was at Eynsford Railway Station, the station porter being the responsible person. Then, one man or girl raked away the chaff from under the thresher—a really dusty job—one man pitched the trusses of straw from the back end of the thresher into an elevator, and, finally, two men built the straw stack. This meant a team of ten people at the threshing, while two more men were occupied carting the sacks of corn back to the farm. The thresher cost 12s. per hour and the straw trusser 15d per hour.

I was often one of the threshing gang and I well remember one particular occasion when, because the feeder was off sick, I was asked to do that important job. It really pleased me. But what I remember most about that day was that Bruce Dollings gave me a £1 note at night for my work. I also remember him saying he couldn't pay that rate the next day. So I was back to the chaff raking!

The decision of when to buy the first combine harvester required very careful consideration. When and how would the grain be dried and stored? Corn stacks in the fields were our present granaries. The practical place to locate a new grain store was at Furlongs Farm close by the existing grass drying plant. This meant that a further area of the apple orchard would be grubbed. James and I were now sufficiently committed to farming at home to become very much involved with any planning or decision making. We visited other grain store installations in Kent and Essex, few as they were, and started our thoughts working; we spent over a year debating the size, shape and layout of the building.

During this period we were growing up in the era of farm mechanization just as schoolchildren of today are growing up with computers. More machines meant more breakdowns, many of which were no longer within the scope of the local blacksmith to

Tractor hay sweep and a model.

deal with. So we converted a building close to the farmhouse into our first workshop, the design and layout being strongly influenced by the Allan tidiness disease. Electric welding that had hitherto been little used or even known on farms was slowly becoming recognized as worthwhile. So with some persuasion, and James and I having a two-to-one voting power with our father, we bought our first electric welder in 1947. Our father so often said to people 'As the boys grow older, they need more expensive toys.' Bob Vinson, a very good mechanically minded farmer, at Swanley bought for us an ex-army American-made mobile welder which had a 30-hp Chrysler petrol engine generating up to 300 amps DC current. The expensive toy was a wise investment which is still giving good service today.

The occasion that sparked off our interest in welding was when we were about to build four new bull boxes with service pens. They were to be constructed with 6-inch iron pipes as posts and 2-inch iron pipes as railings. The 6-inch piping bought was ex-National Fire Service water pipes used in the London streets during the war bombing. The contractor charged £71 for just the welding only—that triggered off the idea of constructing the other pens ourselves. We went to evening lessons on welding given by Bert Salway at his steelworks in Dartford. He laid a good foundation for welding. About that time, the *Power Farmer* magazine had a competition for writing an article, 'How welding helps the farmer'. I was one of the three winners and the prize was a three-week welding course at the Lincoln Arc Welding Co's factory at Welwyn Garden City. It couldn't have been a more opportune time and their course gave me real confidence in welding. In 1950 I received a Certificate of Award from the same company in Ohio, USA, for another article I subsequently wrote and their $50 cheque furnished the tool chest I have had ever since in the kitchen. I realized

The James F. Lincoln

Arc Welding Foundation

Presents

this CERTIFICATE OF AWARD *to*

William G. G. Alexander

for the excellence of his entry

in the Award Program conducted by this Foundation

dedicated to the scientific progress of Arc Welding

Signed *E.E. Dreese*

CHAIRMAN, BOARD OF TRUSTEES

E.E. Dreese, B.S. in E.E., M.S in E.E., E.E.
Chairman Department Electrical Engineering
Ohio State University

October 2, 1950
Cleveland, Ohio

Arc Welding Foundation Certificate of Award to W.G.G. Alexander, Ohio USA, 1950.

that the knowledge of electric arc welding would be a great asset to all future building and construction work.

The plans for building the new grain store ultimately crystalized, and construction began in 1948. We had to obtain a permit for steel for the framework of the building as it was still on allocation after the war. The building was 120 feet long and 80 feet wide. The width consisted of a 40-foot central span and two 20-foot-wide lean-tos. The outside walls of the building and silo walls were built with 9-inch hollow concrete

Furlongs grain store, 1949.

blocks which were made by the farm employees in the adjacent grass-drying shed out of season. The silo walls were reinforced with half-inch steel rods in the hollows which were filled with concrete. Stress and strains were not accurately known, so the silos were built extra strong. During over forty years of use they have not shown any sign of weakness. The silos are 15 feet deep on one side and 10 feet on the other. The sloping floor, which is built on brick piers, is of malting kiln tiles which have 960 holes in each 12 by 12-inch tile. Heated air from a pipe under the floor was blown through the grain to dry it. The conveying of grain was by a pneumatic system, later changed to a 'jog trough' and finally to a concave belt-conveyor, each improvement to give a higher movement rate to match increasing combine outputs.

The platform for the grain cleaner was built of steel, which was very difficult to obtain. However, George Pinkerton, a pig farmer and rhubarb grower in Houston, Renfrewshire, and a friend of my father's, had contacts in the Clyde Shipbuilding Yards. He arranged the despatch to Eynsford of five tons 16 hundredweight of steel beams, at a cost of £15 per ton. They were second-hand, from a ship that was being dismantled, and therefore did not require a steel permit. They had rivet holes all along one side and were slightly curved.

Building the platform was my first major welding construction job, and first of all I made a model for the design to be approved by Mr Smith of Corcoran's, London, the makers of the sieve and double aspirator cleaners. The three-week welding course that I attended certainly proved very worthwhile as there were downhand, vertical and overhead welding joints. I must have made an excellent job as no fractures have ever appeared. The framework for the top grain conveyor was built from wartime Morrison Shelter angle-iron welded together. We bought fifteen tons after the war and some was still being used in 1990. The sixteen grain silos hold 560 tons and one

The grain store, 1949. The big shed 1923, Cattle yards 1936.

lean-to has an on-floor capacity of 300 tons. The grain store with its deep ventilated bins was one of the first of its type to be built in Kent. Apart from contractors building the framework, it was home-made. Although the new grain store was not ready to use until 1949, we bought an Allis-Chalmers All-crop 60 Combine for the 1948 harvest. It was pulled by a tractor and had its own engine to drive the combine mechanism. There were bagging and bulk-grain models. We bought the bagging-off one, and what a busy job it was for two men to bag, tie and slide the bags of grain down a chute onto the stubble. There was also some muscular work needed to cart off the bags to the farm buildings. Nevertheless, there was sheer excitement as well as toil and sweat in having a combine working on the farm. For the next harvest, when the grain store was fully operational, we bought two more combines. Another Allis Chalmers, bulk-grain model, which cost £600, and a Massey-Harris 726, also with a bulk-grain tank, at a cost of £800. This was self-propelled and it seemed heaven-sent, being able to combine in the direction which best suited the condition of the crop.

It soon became evident that it would be prudent to grow other crops for which we could use the combines, and we decided to grow grass for seed production. In our boyhood days, James and I, during our holidays in Scotland, visited friends at a farm where they were growing Ayrshire perennial ryegrass for seed. It was a very profitable crop when the weather at harvesting time was good, but could be a disaster if the weather was bad. Their harvesting methods needed a lot of hand labour. We believed that, by combining direct from a mown swarth and with the better climate of the south-east of England, we would overcome the difficulties our Scottish friends encountered.

In 1954 twenty-three acres of perennial ryegrass, variety S101, which had been bred at Aberystwyth, was undersown in Atle spring wheat. This variety was the first high-yielding spring-sown wheat which had a strong milling character. Its dominance over other varieties lasted for at least fifteen years from 1942. We successfully

Grass seed awards, Toronto Winter Fair.

harvested our first crop of grass seed in 1955. The field was mown at the critical stage of seed ripeness, left to ripen fully in the untouched swarth for about ten days, and then was harvested by the combine with a pick-up attachment. The seed was dried to below 12 per cent moisture content and cleaned through our Corcoran grain cleaner, which made a fairish job but could not attain the 98 per cent purity required for certification; the final cleaning had to be done in a seed merchant's warehouse.

In 1967 we managed to acquire a second-hand pair of indented cylinders and were fortunate in having space in the grain store to construct a platform for them, adjacent to a grain elevator. Since then with some skill and lots of patience in the setting of these cylinders, we have consistently produced certifiable seed.

At the same time as the grass-seed cylinders were installed we also bought a pair of cylinders suitable for grain. They enabled us to clean the home-grown cereals to a higher standard before powder dressing with our Strickland Dresser (see p. 51).

The handling of grain in bulk soon became commonplace once there was the option to buy combines with either bagging-off spouts or bulk-grain tanks. It therefore became logical to sell grain in bulk instead of the standard four-bushel Starkey Room sacks which held 2¼ hundredweight of wheat. In 1957 we were one of the earlier farmers in Kent to have bulkgrain loading facilities from overhead bins direct into lorries. We constructed three ten-ton bins which could empty their contents in under five minutes. It was a great treat to watch a lorry being loaded! We determined the unloading height of our bins by the height of the lowest railway bridge in our area.

The decrease of available labour, and a very much larger acreage of grain being grown during the war, saw an increase in the number of combines in use countrywide to 2,500 by 1944. In 1949 Massey-Harris began manufacturing combines at a factory in Kilmarnock, Ayrshire, and there were more than ten thousand combines in operation for the 1950 harvest. By 1960 the estimated numbers had rocketed to over

W. Lillico lorry being loaded from bulk grain bins, 1957.

fifty thousand, a tremendous change in only sixteen years. The number in use by 1990 had not changed significantly but the cutting width, capacity and overall size had increased enormously.

The rapid expansion in the number of combines being used after the war brought an ever-increasing volume of grain onto the market at harvest time, and naturally prices bottomed. The effect of this was that new grain stores began mushrooming all over the country. This gave farmers the opportunity to market the grain at more advantageous prices later in the year.

Another consequence of more combines was, quite naturally, the demise of the faithful threshing machine. A very small acreage of wheat was still being cut by a binder and threshed just for the purpose of obtaining thatching straw—not, as before, for thatching haystacks and corn stacks but for cottages and barns, particularly listed buildings.

Bruce Dollings, the threshing contractor in Eynsford, gave up his business in 1962. The rubber-tyred tractors which moved and drove the threshing machines had a market value but the threshing machines had no buyers. It seems a criminal thought today that they were set alight in a field, and that their only value was as scrap iron. That is the price we have to pay for progress.

CHAPTER 13
The third generation in harness

As a result of wartime circumstances my brother and I did not have the opportunity to attend an agricultural college, but we had a very good tutor at home to teach us practical farming. After leaving Dartford Grammar School in the summer of 1938, James did however attend an agricultural day-class once a week at Tonbridge School. He and Allison Jackson, a neighbouring farmer's son and classmate, both learnt much about the theories of farming which they found most useful. I left school two years later than James; and as it was during the war went straight into harness. Our father handed over the reins quite readily to us when we were in our early twenties but occasionally, when we were getting out of step with practicalities and realities, he would take hold of the reins again and pull quite hard and deliberately on the bit. That taught us to become fairly hard-mouthed!

Every day we discussed the work programme, and James and I alternated weekly at being the one in charge and giving the men their daily orders. I sometimes wonder which week I enjoyed most – being the boss or being the boy?

Our involvement in running the day-to-day affairs, enabled our father to devote more of this time to the livestock, which he especially enjoyed. He also delighted in giving advice and opinions to young farmers in the district and would call on them regularly to have a 'wee blether'.

The dairy herds had been subjected to a lot of disturbance during the war due to enemy action, and milk yields had consequently suffered. My father was very keen to rear young bulls for sale and he decided to engage two new herdsmen. In 1945 Leslie Puxty became the new herdsman at Manor Farm. The existing herd was sold in April of that year and the cowshed was modernized on the same lines as the improvements at Castle Farm the previous year. The new Manor Farm herd consisted entirely of home-bred autumn-calving Friesian heifers. In the autumn of 1946 Neville Free was engaged as herdsman at Castle Farm. It was very soon noticeable how the herd yields increased dramatically thanks to the skill of these two herdsmen and to 'the load of encouragement that the Guv'nor gave us,' as Neville Free said.

The first bull that Neville Free reared was Eynsford Keemaus, which was sold for 580 guineas at the Friesian Society's Annual Bull Show and Sale at Reading in 1947. He was reserve for the Thornton Cup (Bull under 18 months old). This was a great start for Neville. A year later the bull's full brother, Eynsford Maymar, sold for 1100 guineas. Another bull from the same dam, Eynsford May 20th RM,* won the Thornton Cup at the Society's Sale in 1953 and was sold for 2,200 guineas. It is often said that success breeds success. The sale of Eynsford-bred bulls certainly reached

*RM denotes an award for high milk and butterfat achievement; RML is awarded to cows yielding over 50 tons of milk.

William Alexander and Neville Free received the Thornton Cup at Reading 5th November, 1953.

their zenith the following year at the Society's Bull Show and Sale, Reading, in November 1954. Eynsford Anker 13th, born 15 May 1953 was sold for 5,000 guineas to Mr F. J. Luttrel in Somerset. This was a record price and was unbeaten for fourteen years. Both my father and Neville Free richly deserved the success which they had achieved. The same bull also won the Butterfat Challenge Trophy, one for which my father had been striving for many years. Much of the demand for Eynsford-bred bulls was attributed to the 'bred-in' butterfat, as my father called it, he himself being known, as mentioned earlier, as the Butterfat King because of his policy of breeding from high butterfat cattle, and his preaching of that gospel for many years.

Eynsford Anker 13th's dam, Eynsford Dewberry 28th RM, RML was a remarkable cow having given over 2,000 gallons in each of the 5th, 6th, 7th and 8th lactations with an average butterfat content of 4.07 per cent. In 1953 she won the Harold Jackson Trophy which is awarded nationally to the cow of any breed which gains the highest number of points assessed from the milk, butterfat and calving index of three successive lactations.

Eynsford Anker 13th's sire, Eynsford (imp. 1950) Butenmoark Anker, was bred in Holland and was one of the 57 bulls which were imported to improve the British Friesian. The sale was held at Peterborough on 20 November 1950 and was naturally of tremendous interest to breeders. Seventeen bulls were allocated to AI centres, and forty were sold by auction. At the time of this momentous sale, which was attended by over 3,000 people, our father was unwell and was confined to bed. James and I, with our two herdsmen, went to the preview of the bulls at Peterborough in order to select a suitable one to buy. We came back with our considered opinions of two choices. We

Eynsford Anker 13th. Won the Butterfat Trophy and sold for 5,000 guineas at Reading 5th November, 1953.

Lord Hudson presents Butterfat Trophy to William Alexander.

William Alexander and cousin Jack Steven at a sale at Crewe.

discussed with our father the price that we should be prepared to bid for a bull and it was settled at up to 2,000 guineas. There was an exciting atmosphere on sale day and breeders were keeping their interests tight to their chests. As the sale progressed we could foresee that prices would be well over our target, so James and I put our heads together and convinced each other, that we had been allotted 2,000 guineas each to spend. The auctioneers hammer fell on our final bid of 4,000 guineas for the bull we had marked in our catalogue, Butenmoark Anker. When we arrived back home to tell the good tidings, our father never raised an eyebrow about the price—it would have been too late anyway!

This 1950 importation added many qualities which were lacking in the British Friesians at that time and so the progeny of these bulls became very fashionable. It must also be said that, as with all young unproven bulls, there were many disappointments, as some bulls carried the red recessive gene and others transmitted abnormalities. Some progeny were disappointing in regard to udders and milk yields, but there was considerable improvement in the standard of confirmation, particularly hind legs and also in butterfat. The importation gave a tremendous boost to the Artificial Insemination centres and then to the demand for young bulls. Eynsford-bred bulls were bought by the English and Scottish Milk Marketing Boards and Cambridge and Hampshire AI Centres.

Northern Ireland and the Republic of Ireland, which are large milk producers, had many AI stations and besides competing with each other they were very strong contenders with the UK buyers at the Bull sales at Reading. From 1957 to 1970 they bought eleven Eynsford bulls. James and I together with Allen Brooks, a Friesian enthusiast who had a herd of cows and a retail milk round in Seal, visited the AI centres in Ireland on many occasions and so kept in touch with the buyers. Their pace

Ron Palmer with Eynsford Vera 8th exhibited at Olympia.

Judging in progress at an early Dairy Show held in a London street.

Eynsford Eclipse 143rd Supreme Champion Kent Show. Lord Cornwallis presents cups to James Alexander and herdsman Ken Read.

of life was much slower than ours and, on our first few visits, milk was still being taken by donkey carts to their co-operative creameries. Latterly it was by car or van with a trailer behind. Their keenness to breed improved cattle however was equal to that in the UK.

Our herdsmen were keen exhibitors at the Royal Dairy Show at Olympia in London and the Kent Show held at Maidstone. The most prestigious awards which they won were first prize Inspection and first prize Milking Trials at Olympia in 1960 with Eynsford Vera 8th, a first calf heifer that gave 70.2 lbs milk at 4.29 per cent butter fat, exhibited by Ron Palmer; and, at the Kent Show in July 1978, Eynsford Eclipse 143rd won the Supreme Championship award and was exhibited by Ken Read.

Besides sending yearling bulls to auction sales, many were sold privately to breeders and some as young calves. Several were sold to buyers as far away as Scotland and

Eynsford Station before lines were electrified.

Bull calf prepared for travel by rail.

were sent by rail at about six weeks of age. In those early days there was no difficulty in sending them from Eynsford Station via Euston to Glasgow and from there to their final destination. A calf travelled in the guard's van and was provided with food and water.

Prior to its journey, the calf was halter-trained for two days so that it was used to being led and tied up. On the morning of its travel, the calf was despatched in a

Lucerne breeding plants.

three-bushel-thick hessian bag which acted as a large nappy. Four holes were cut in the bag for its legs and the top of the sacking was tied front and back to make handles. The calf was therefore nice and snug for the journey.

The calf was taken to Eynsford Station for the 7.50am train to London to be in time for the 10.00am Euston to Glasgow train. The passengers at Eynsford were always highly amused and interested to see a calf waiting for 'their' train but pleased to know it travelled in the guard's van. Before the railway was electrified on 6th January 1935, we used to carry the calf across the railway lines to the 'up side'. After electrification the calf had to be encouraged to walk over the bridge. Latterly calves went by road transport when the railways stopped this service.

Another interest which our father was able to pursue with more attention and vigour, because we boys were at home, was the breeding of a new variety of lucerne. This legume is particularly suited to being grown on alkaline soils. It has a deep rooting system, three feet or more, and is therefore able to withstand dry periods particularly well, and really does proliferate in hot sunny weather.

The rotation of crops at Eynsford during the 1940s and before, included lucerne in selected fields, its production was for a period of five years. Good husbandry preparations were essential to reap a rewarding crop. For the best establishment, the lucerne was undersown in spring wheat, the crop in the previous year having been savoys or cabbages which had received a heavy dressing of farmyard manure. The field for lucerne was therefore clean and in good heart—no chemicals at all were used for weed control. It was essential to inoculate the seed with bacteria if lucerne hadn't been grown previously in that field. Three cuts of lucerne were taken each year for the five years and this gave a tremendous dry-matter yield, far in excess of other fodder crops. The variety sown for many years was Provence which was produced in that region of France. The vigour of the crop, however, varied widely from the sowing in different years; good some years, indifferent others.

As a start to the lucerne-breeding programme, seed was saved from a good production area in one field. Our trial ground was established the following year with over 300 single plants. The growing characteristics of each plant throughout the year were individually recorded, particular note being taken of early growth, good re-growth after first and second cuts, bushy and dense foliage and large succulent leaves. The unwanted types were rogued out over a period of three years. This left a small family of highly productive plants which were seeded in their fourth year. This procedure was repeated for several years and the resultant seed was then multiplied in quantity. The commercial crops of lucerne grown on our farm from this seed achieved far superior results compared with the previous varieties, and from these results my father believed that Eynsford Lucerne would have a place in the market.

Enquiries were made at the National Institute of Agricultural Botany at Cambridge, asking if they would include Eynsford Lucerne in their trial plots. This they readily agreed to. The lucerne trials, under the watchful eye of Mr A. Zaleski, the head of that department, lasted for a three-year period and the 1956, 1957 and 1958 trials consisted of nine varieties, including Eynsford,—which was the only British-bred variety. The tabulated results gave the total dry matter and total protein for each of the years and finally the three years' total. It was Eynsford Lucerne that came top of the list; it had out-yielded all the other eight varieties. In comparison with Provence Lucerne it yielded a 41 per cent increase in the total dry matter and 54 per cent increase in protein. Following these results, Eynsford Lucerne was included by the NIAB in their list of Recommended Varieties.

The lucerne seed which we combined was not ready to harvest until late September and at times it was even into early November. This was not satisfactory for a consistent production of large quantities of seed for sale and we therefore made arrangements with our agents, Messrs Hurst's of Essex, to have our stock seed multiplied in America where sunshine was guaranteed and irrigation was available. James and I on separate occasions went over to California to ensure that the isolation of the crops and promotion of the seed was satisfactory. Large quantities of high-germination certified seed were produced there for several years, and were sold in many European countries as well as in the UK.

Our breeding programme was continuous and we produced an improved strain which we named Monarch. The registration of new varieties at this time was controlled by the EEC regulation which had been adopted, and we found that the procedure would be too costly for us as private breeders and there was no guarantee of success. In due course other varieties from the seedhouses overtook the Eynsford variety. We were, however, very proud to have held our position for several years. The top of a ladder is always a shaky place.

The hop scene in 1944 was in a mood for change, triggered off by the introduction of new varieties of hops. Professor E. S. Salmon of Wye College was in charge of breeding from 1907 and continued this work for nearly fifty years. Two of the outstanding varieties released for farm production were Brewers Gold C9A(1934) and Bullion Q43 (1938). The four growers with the greatest enthusiasm for the new Wye Varieties were William Alexander, Arthur Amos, Robert Boucher and Percy Chambers, and all were disgusted by the low valuations being put on their hops. At a meeting in Maidstone, on 29 March 1944, they formed the Association of Growers of New Varieties of Hops (AGNVH). Its objects were to encourage the good growing of the best new varieties and their good drying and packing; to encourage growers to mark each pocket with the name of the new variety and to obtain chemical analysis of the hops; to encourage growers to increase the acreage of suitable varieties; and to

Pockets of Bullion hops from Castle Farm at Norwich Brewery.

endeavour to obtain valuations of the New Varieties commensurate with their brewing value. These objects were to be achieved by farm walks and an annual exhibition of dried samples. The first exhibition of New Varieties was organized by Wigan, Richardson & Co. under the auspices of the Institute of Brewing, and held in January 1945.

I am very happy to record that the principles made by those four stalwart growers continue to be practised today and that the AGNVH has published an *Annual Booklet* since their first meeting. It is read with great interest world-wide.

We continued to grow Brewers Gold until 1959 and Bullion until 1985 when they were replaced by Northern Brewer and Wye Northdown. The different varieties gave a spread of hop training times and optimum picking dates; also, the disease risk was spread with having different varieties, an important aspect in such a disease-vulnerable crop. From 1945 we grew 50 per cent Fuggle hops and 50 per cent New Varieties.

I became a committee member of the AGNVH when my father retired and I was Chairman in 1959 and 1960. I succeeded Jim Worley, who was Chairman the two previous years. Peter Day, John Paine, Jim Worley and I are the longest-serving members of that committee and we have all witnessed many ups and downs in the growing and marketing of hops of both old and New Varieties. In 1994 the AGNVH will be celebrating its half century.

Our acreage of hops remained steady at 18 acres until we changed from hand-picking to machine-picking in 1960. Each year after the war we had to employ more and more pickers for this same acreage. In 1946 we increased the number of hopper huts by twenty to eighty-six. These additional huts were ex-Army huts and cost a mere £120. They were roomier than the other huts, so could accommodate larger families. Our hop picking lasted about four weeks and needed 200 pickers. They mostly came from the dock areas of London and they really enjoyed hop picking in the country fresh air; it was their annual holiday and they could earn some money as at that time they did not have holidays with pay. Their children marvelled at the freedom of the countryside and back at school they could boast about their experiences at scrumping apples—great fun unless you were caught. Once holidays with pay became more general our hop pickers' camp looked more like a holiday camp than a hop pickers' camp. We therefore took a fresh look at the decision of whether to build even more huts or to pick the hops by machine. Hop-picking machines were gaining favour in the 1950s and an acceptable sample of hops could be produced, although in the early days there was the need to hand-pick some leaves and strigs off the final belt. It was therefore decided with some sadness and subsequently much joy that 1959 was to be the last year of hand picking, and so we installed our hop-picking machine in readiness for the 1960 harvest. The economics of so doing were absolutely correct.

Although wartime farming was very onerous there were some social functions and money-raising events held in the villages, many of them for the benefit of the Red Cross. Dig for Victory had encouraged people to make more effort in cultivating their gardens and allotments to produce food. As a result of this, the Eynsford Allotment Holders and Gardeners Association was revived in 1942 under the chairmanship of Mr C. M. Hever, with Mr L. U. Judge, the Parish Council clerk, as secretary. Their first Produce Show was held in September of that year and gardeners competed against each other with tremendous enthusiasm and zest. The pride of exhibiting the longest runner beans, largest onions or best-shaped carrots was well worth all the effort in growing and preparing them for exhibiting. The show was hailed as a great success. Once it was over many of the exhibits were kindly left to be sold by auction.

Certificate of Merit Red Cross Agricultural Fund, 1944.

VE day celebrations 14 July, 1945. Me and my girl and my dog.

Farmers supplemented the produce for sale and considerable sums of money were raised for the Red Cross. The Produce Show has continued as an annual event. Reg Morgan became chairman in 1948, a position he has occupied ever since—a tremendous credit to him. My brother and I have been involved with the show for fifty years. Our regular duties have been for me to auction the produce and for James to collect the money. The auction with village people bidding against each other, encouraged by the auctioneer, is such a fun event.

The old custom of having a Harvest Supper was revived in 1944. Land Girls acted as waitresses and they certainly gave a welcome harvest atmosphere to the evening. Local talent provided the entertainment after the supper each year. In 1945 I was able to show off my skills of conjuring, an accomplishment which I learnt whilst at school. I also gave shows to Sunday School parties and at children's birthdays.

The end of the war in 1945 was a time for countrywide celebrations. Towns and villages arranged their own events. Eynsford had a sports day with fun fair and side shows. Those events were preceded by a parade of decorated vehicles through the village to the recreation ground. James and I had an entry with our milk round tricycle painted red, white and blue with a tall platform we built on the back. On top of this rode our Welsh corgi, Alfie. He was dressed in a red, white and blue jacket and cap. We were well disguised and our entry was called 'Me and my Girl and my Dog. Alfie had little fear of heights and a very good sense of balance. I had trained him to stay perched on a single strand of fencing wire which my mother used as a clothes drying line. John Topham, of photographic fame, took his picture on this wire and Alfie's photo received wide coverage in the London evening and local newspapers. One caption read: 'A dog with a well-balanced diet'.

Alfie balancing on wire.

CHAPTER 14
Following in Father's footsteps

In November 1943 I went with my father to Scotland. His first call was to a seed potato grower in Angus; then a visit to have a blether with John Mackie at Laurencekirk. In 1936 my father and his cousin Jack Steven called by chance on John Mackie who had made an excellent sack elevator. They persuaded him to make one and send it to Eynsford—which he did. It was built with Scottish ingenuity: the base was wooden slats fixed across two chains off a muck-spreader and driven by an electric motor. The mounting on four rubber-tyred wheels gave easy manoeuvrability. Our prime purpose for the elevator was to load two-hundredweight Starkey Room sacks of barley onto lorries. The elevator's delivery height allowed the lorry driver to take the sack straight onto his back for loading. This saved an immense amount of huffing and puffing and struggling. The bulk handling of grain in the early 1950s gave the elevator an early retirement and eased men's backs.

The next call, following our visit to John Mackie, was to Willie McKendric and John Houston, both near Paisley, from whom my father had bought many bull calves. We were taken through the byre and to fields where cattle were grazing and were told each animal's pedigree, milk yields and butterfat record, and its life history. My father selected a cow whose confirmation and pedigree were what he was looking for and agreed a price for the next bull calf she had. This was my first visit to see how the Scots traded and I remember being most impressed by their attention to detail and by the tidiness of their steadings (farmyard and buildings). It was a good education for me having had three years at home since leaving school.

Our stay for the next three days was with my cousins in the neighbouring town of Beith, which I knew well from school holiday days there. I so clearly remember going out the next morning to watch my cousin Robert Allan ploughing a grass field with two horses pulling a single-furrow plough and taking only a 7-inch wide furrow. The turned-over turf was treated with such respect that if one piece did not lie over correctly Robert would go back and tread it into place. That seemed much too pernickety to me. He was, as one would expect, making a super job—but, oh dear me, speed was not the order of the day; I just hadn't been brought up at Home Farm to such a snail's pace. The ploughing did, however, leave the furrows set up beautifully for hand-sowing the oats in the spring, and with a set of one-horse harrows, the seeds were covered over superbly (I must in fairness mention that once tractors had become accepted on farms in the district a few years later, Robert changed horses for tractors and fairly got a move-on!)

The climax of my stay with Robert and his sister Janet was however, going to a Young Farmers' Club dance in the neighbouring village of Lochwinnoch. Robert was on the committee running the dance and was 'on the door' that evening so I was quite on my own amongst other young men in the hall. It was traditional at the YFC dances for all the girls to be seated on one side of the dance floor and all the boys to stand on the other side. I couldn't help feeling conspicuous as I was the only one in a brown suit (I didn't buy another brown suit for years!). A list of the Scottish dances for the evening was displayed and I soon learnt that the boys made 'bookings'. No sooner did the MC announce the next dance than the boys crossed the hall in a mass to dance with the girl of their choice (if they were lucky). Apart from dancing with Janet and two other cousins, Mary and Isa Allan, I spotted two nice lassies who were sisters and they took my eye. Eventually I managed to dance with each of them. They were Margaret and Marion Lamont and they knew my cousins very well. I took a great fancy to the younger sister, Marion, but I could hardly have envisaged at that time that we would be married seven years later. A true example of love at first sight and at first dance.

Marion and Margaret had an elder brother, John, and a younger one, Douglas. Their father and mother kept a shop and a small dairy herd of Ayrshire cows right in the town of Paisley. There were also quite a number of other cowkeepers with byres and shops in the town. The grazing pastures were, naturally, some distance away. Mr Lamont drove his cows down the back streets to the fields, which were just over a mile from the byre. There was the odd occasion on the trek to the fields when a cow went in through a shop door and caused some excitement within.

Mr Lamont was an early riser and started milking at 4 a.m. so that the milk was ready to sell that morning. He had eighteen cows, and one milker from the town gave a hand. Mrs Lamont baked scones, crumpets, pancakes and tattie scones every day to sell in the shop. J & P Coats' Cotton and Thread mills were a major industry in Paisley and the mill girls on their way to work early in the morning would call regularly at Lamont's Dairy to buy the freshly baked goods. John had a retail milk round and was

Mr Lamont takes 18 cows along town road to the pastures.

Margaret and Marion Lamont at Home Farm, August, 1950.

often helped by Marion, while Margaret and Marion both helped their mother in the shop, and in doing so acquired the knack of chatting which they were good at all their lives. Their younger brother Douglas was still at school at that time; later in life he had a dairy farm in Lochwinnoch and kept a herd of Friesian cows.

My visits to Scotland after this one with my father were for quite a different purpose and I went to the YFC dances in the winters with my brother James and my sister Mary on many occasions. Marion's first visit to Home Farm was in 1945 with my cousin Janet; it was at the time of the VE celebrations in London, and we were all in the crowd that evening outside Buckingham Palace, cheering the King and Queen as they waved to the crowd from their balcony. A memorable day for Marion's first visit.

Canal Street Dairy. 1938 Austin milk delivery motor.

In January 1950 we made up a party of six for a skiing holiday in Switzerland. There were Marion Lamont and her cousin Margaret Hamilton, whose parents also had a dairy shop in Paisley, Harold Dinnis, a neighbouring farmer from Shoreham, and James, Mary and me. There was great excitement for all of us, going on our first time to ski. The 26-hour journey started by train from Eynsford to Victoria and then to Dover; the cross-Channel ferry boat to Calais was followed by a long train journey with sleepers to Basle, where we arrived at 4 a.m. We thoroughly enjoyed an excellent breakfast there in the spotlessly clean railway station restaurant. Another train journey took us the short distance to Lake Lucerne, which we crossed by ferry, and our final train journey was up the snow-covered mountans to the skiing resort of Engelberg. We were met by the travel agent courier who had arranged a horse and sleigh ride on the snow-covered roads to the Hotel Hess. The surrounding scenery made us think we had arrived in fairy land—it was beautiful. We had made this long journey with only light hand luggage: our well-filled trunk and other cases, which we had last seen at Victoria Station, were in the hotel foyer awaiting our arrival—marvellous!

We thoroughly enjoyed the ten days of skiing and the aprés ski, and also tobogganing. The air was very exhilarating, the food was excellent (black tie and long dress for dinner in the evening) and the company was excellent. Our parents were quite anxious about us being away on this new sport and very pleased to see us all return safe and well.

The six of us went skiing again in January 1951, this time to Pontresina, also in Switzerland, and we all equally enjoyed the holiday. Marion and I had a special reason for enjoyment as we had become engaged in May 1950. On one of the days we took a local train to see the ski-jumping at St Moritz, and Marion and I took the occasion to buy her wedding ring in St Moritz—it was a truly exciting day for us both. After we returned home from another super skiing holiday, the time passed by very quickly as Marion and I prepared for our wedding.

Ski-ing party Switzerland, 1950.

We were married in St George's Church, Paisley, on 18 April 1951. The wedding reception was held in Paisley Town Hall. The cutting of the cake to wish the bride and bridegroom good health and happiness took place in the reception room before we sat down to a five-course dinner. The speeches followed and then there was the traditional Scottish dancing late into the evening. When we were leaving and saying our farewells, I was lifted shoulder high and taken to the taxi whilst Marion was sedately escorted by her two bridesmaids. We spent our first night in the romantic setting of Loch Lomond, from where we toured the North of Scotland right up to John O'Groats, before making our journey south and arriving at Castle Farm ten days later.

We were given a great welcome at our new home by family and friends. I carried my bride across the threshold, and so began a very happy marriage; we lived at Castle Farmhouse for thirty-four years.

Our wedding seemed to trigger off two more in the family. James married Diana Pierce in April 1952, and my twin sister Mary married Stanley Tassell in November 1953.

Diana had two younger sisters, Sheila and Margaret, and two brothers, William and Richard. Her father, Fred Pierce, had a large fruit farm near Borough Green growing apples, pears, plums and cherries, as well as strawberries and gooseberries. He married Agnes Fife in 1924, the Fife family being very well-known farmers in the Kemsing–Yaldham area. Her father and mother, James and Jane Fife, came to Kent from Ayrshire in 1898. They had been farming in Kilbirne, which neighbours Beith and were well-known to my grandparents. When in Kent they made frequent visits to each other's farms. Jane Fife, who had seven children, was a well-loved Scottish character and became known in her later years as Granny Fife. She died in 1961 at the age of ninety-two and was never happier than when she was surrounded by her eleven grandchildren accompanied by the great-grandchildren.

James and Diana's wedding was held at St Mary's Platt Church and they spent their honeymoon touring France. They have lived all their married life at Meadow View, Lullingstone Lane, just close by Home Farm.

My sister Mary was at Dartford Grammar School for Girls until 1938 and then continued her education in Edinburgh at Craigmount School, which had boarders as well as day girls. It was a very highly respected school known to one of my mother's Scottish relations. At the end of the first summer term in 1939, I went to Edinburgh to escort her home. The headmistress, Miss Ross, knew of my coming and kindly invited me to the end-of-term school outing with the upper forms to a theatre in the evening. I do not remember the title of the play but I do have a clear recollection of being seated at the end of a row next to my sister which was rather tantalizing with so many girls just arm's length away. I stayed for two nights in Edinburgh with Dr W. S. Gordon, whom my father knew. He was head of a department of Moredun Animal Disease Research Station and later became the Director of the Agricultural Research Council station at Compton in Berkshire.

When Mary returned to Scotland for the autumn term, the school had been evacuated to Scone Palace because of the war. Scone Palace, just one mile north of Perth, is steeped in history and claims to be the most historic place in Scotland. It was the crowning place of Scottish kings and the seat of government in Pictish times.

The Stone of Destiny was brought to Scone in the year 843 by Kenneth McAlpine, King of Scots. The last king to be crowned on Scottish soil at Scone was Charles II in 1651. King Robert the Bruce was crowned there in 1306. In 1296 the Stone of Destiny was seized by Edward I in an unsuccessful attempt to rout the Scots and prevent further coronations at Scone. It was taken to Westminster Abbey where it was placed under the Coronation Chair and still remains there as an emblem of Royal state.

Just in front of Scone Palace Chapel is a mound called the Moot Hill (or Boot Hill). It was constructed in the Dark Ages, traditionally by earth brought from all parts of the realm. When the kings of Scotland were crowned at Scone, they should have toured Scotland to receive allegiance from their chiefs and lairds. As they could not afford to keep the necessary bodyguard to protect them against kidnapping or assassination, it was decreed that the chiefs should come to Scone to the coronations.

This they did, filling their boots before they left home, so legend has it, with their own earth and thus standing on their own land they swore fealty to the kings and afterwards ceremoniously emptied their boots on Moot Hill.

The teaching at Scone Palace was very intensive and, as one can well imagine, Scottish history in particular was a subject which was taught with great feeling and thoroughness. The war affected science lessons as there were no lab facilities, and instead of being waited upon at meal times, the girls had to take their turn at washing-up and helping with various chores. Mary spent just one more year at Craigmount School and then returned home to help our mother in the house and with general farm duties.

A modest number of eggs were hatched and the chicks reared for the hen batteries which supplied eggs for the retail milk round. Ducks were also reared for the family's Sunday lunch. A pig was kept to utilize any waste food and in due course supplemented the meat ration. Mary helped with messages and the collection and delivery of a multitude of farm items. At hop picking in September she was the bookie who wrote down the number of bushels of hops picked at each picker's bin or basket for the three measurings each day. She said she thoroughly enjoyed those four weeks every year. She also enjoyed chatting to the oast workers and in the evening would often go to the hop pickers' huts and chat with them around their camp fires.

Moot Hill, Scone Palace Chapel.

Mary married Stanley Tassell on 11 November 1953 at St Martins Church, Eynsford, and they began their married life at Knole Hill House, Ulcombe, seven miles south-east of Maidstone. The Tassell family are well known in that area, having farmed in the district since before the 1800s. Stanley's father and uncle farmed a large acreage of apples, damsons and plums, as well as 40 acres of strawberries and 30 acres of hops. Fruit and hops were a very traditional combination on the clay soils in the Weald of Kent. They also had a flock of 500 Border Leicester x Suffolk Ram breeding ewes, again very traditional on their type of farm.

It was in the relatively short period of two and a half years that we three in the family had all married and left home. Our father and mother continued to live at Home Farm and to be involved in the farm business. James and I made the management decisions and our father generously gave us the option of taking his

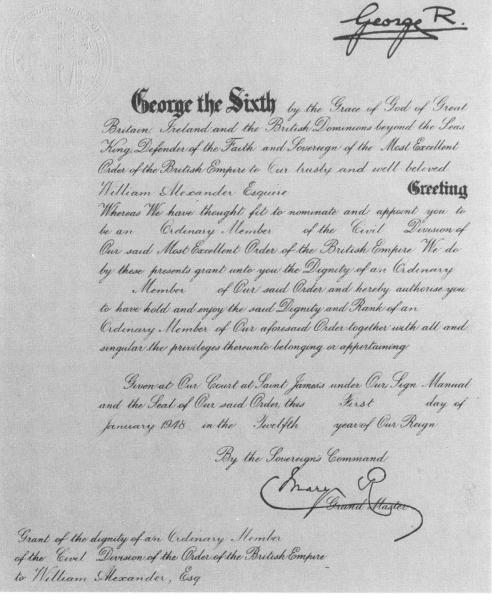

William Alexander M.B.E. 1st January 1948.

advice or not. We learnt by our mistakes. We were each responsible for the day-to-day running of our own sections of the farms. Our mother was never happier than when keeping the farm books and this she continued to do until the age of eighty, latterly with an increasing amount of assistance. She was also very keen to continue traditions, one of which was having a family Sunday lunch at Home Farm. This took place for many years until the grandchildren began to outnumber the adults. By 1960 there were eleven grandchildren, all healthy and very lively, and all born within a seven-year period (see Appendix V—family tree).

Unhappily, their grandfather did not live to see them all born because our father died on 8 March 1957 at the age of seventy-four. There were a great many tributes paid to him about his skilful farming techniques and methods and the willingness with which he imparted his knowledge to anyone he knew and to others who came to seek his advice.

He received a great honour for his farming ability and inventiveness with the award of the MBE in King George VI's New Year's Honours list on 1 January 1948. It was rare for a practical farmer to receive such an award and its announcement was greeted with tremendous acclaim by people in all walks of life and the farming fraternity in particular. He gave talks about his practical farming methods to discussion group meetings all over the country. He knew his subject so well that he never used notes. Mr A. G. Street, a well-known author and broadcaster who also wrote an article each week in the *Farmers' Weekly* used the heading one week 'The habit of being right' for a tribute to the character and farming of William Alexander.

Our father's death ended sixty-five years of the first two generations of the Alexanders farming in the Darent Valley but happily he had known that there were already two more generations to follow him.

CHAPTER 15
Land purchase opportunities

Many successful farmers during their lifetime do not only till the land and market its produce, but also keep an ear to the ground and an eye open for the opportunity to rent or to buy additional land and also to buy and sell properties.

The term or length of a tenancy has, from time to time, been affected by the passing of Agricultural Acts. Before the Second World War, an agricultural tenancy would normally be for a term of years, beyond which little security was provided to the tenant farmer. However, due to the general availability of farms to rent, many tenancies were readily renewed by landlords. After the war two important Acts were passed. The Agricultural Act 1947 dealt with many aspects of the industry and it laid a framework for the Agricultural Holdings Act 1948. This confirmed long-term security of tenure upon all tenants and was generally to the benefit of tenant farmers. During the 1950s and 1960s, this legislation worked well and tenanted farms continued to change hands regularly. The Miscellaneous Provisions Acts of 1976 extended the security of tenure of tenant farmers from not just the lifetime of the original tenant but also to two successive generations of his family, providing such decendants were suitable to farm the holding. This immediately dried up the supply of tenanted farms. Some sense was, however, restored by the Agricultural Holdings Act 1986, which reintroduced the concept of tenancies being for the lifetime of one tenant only and also endeavoured to link rental values to the earning capacity of farms.

We have been fortunate on many occasions to have been able to buy land of which we were the tenant when the landlord decided to sell. Also there were times when we could purchase land which adjoined our own.

One of the earliest purchases was only fourteen acres of Furlongs Farm in 1922. It was good fertile soil and upon completion of the purchase it was planted with fruit trees. Eleven years later, in 1933, Manor Farm, Farningham, having 126 acres, was bought. My father had been the tenant there since 1925. It was a compact dairy farm with reasonably suitable buildings comprising a tithe barn which could house 32 cows, a cart lodge and two farm cottages.

The next significant purchase was Castle Farm, Shoreham, in 1948 following the death of the owner Lord Mildmay (Chapter 9 describes the tenancy which started in 1932). The 316 acres were being cropped with hops, fruit and arable. There was a dairy herd of 40 cows which grazed the river meadows.

Three years later, in 1951, 180 acres of the Eynsford Mount Estate were bought. This was very chalky Grade III land which lay between Bower Lane, Eynsford and Beesfield Lane, Farningham, and had been owned by a building speculator. As its building prospects had come to nought, we came into its possession. It was bare land,

Burning shed of empty boxes, Hulberry Farm.

there were no buildings, and it presented a challenge to grow profitable crops on the thin chalky soil.

In 1952, the Kemp Town Brewery, Brighton, Ltd, who owned Home Farm, having bought it from the Lullingstone Estate in 1934 as a speculation for a London airport, were ready to sell the land. So Home Farm, Eynsford, of which the Alexander family had been tenants since 1891 was added to our ownership, together with some adjoining land, making a total of 320 acres.

Following our father's death in 1957, James and I decided to mark time for a period, even if local farms were for sale. So it was not until 1964 that the next purchase of land took place. This was when Hulberry Farm was bought. There were 110 acres planted with fruit trees, many being rather old and way past their best. The farm had a farmhouse which many years previously had been a pair of cottages, two quite substantial farm buildings and the sites of two cottages which had fallen into disrepair. Hulberry Farm was adjacent to Lullingstone Park and adjoined Home Farm, so purchasing it was very prudent. The soil was of good depth, otherwise fruit trees would not have been planted. The Ministry of Agriculture had a fruit tree grubbing scheme in vogue at that time and with little hesitation we decided to grub the total acreage in readiness to farm the open land. A contractor using a bulldozer made fairly light work of pushing out the trees and burning them, along with heaps of old apple boxes and several dilapidated wooden sheds in which boxes were stored. It took some years to rid the land of the well-established couch grass and the straying tree roots, but in due course the land was brought back into good heart and grew profitable crops. Little did we envisage that Hulberry Farm would be the prime site of a large dairy unit, which we built in 1971/72.

In 1965, the year after buying Hulberry Farm, Eynsford Nurseries was on the market for sale. It was owned by Mr Henry Hutt who had sold his flower nursery land at Swanley for building and then built new glasshouses, a packing shed and a bungalow in Eynsford. The land was opposite the Common Meadow and on one side abutted the Plough public house and on the other side, Furlongs Farm which we owned. Although neither James nor I were conversant with growing flowers and tomatoes under glass and in the open, we were attracted to the opportunity to buy this nursery, which, as one might say, was right on our doorstep.

James had two sons and one daughter and I had two sons and two daughters. We took the long-term view that should any of them be interested in nursery work here would be the chance for them to have a business of their own. So we bought Eynsford Nurseries.

Lower Austin Lodge farm, Eynsford, was rented from Mr F. C. Hynard in 1971. There were 270 acres of arable land and 50 acres of woodland. It had been farmed by his youngest son Gordon until Gordon's sudden death in the summer of 1970. Mr Hynard was the enthusiastic photographer who made that marvellous film of Eynsford before the war and one which has been shown on BBC television as well as in Eynsford Village Hall several times. Mr Hynard died in 1980 at the age of ninety-six and we bought the farm in 1985.

A small farm, New Barn Farm, Lullingstone, was bought in 1973. It belonged to the Lullingstone Estate and we had rented the 61 acres since 1922. The sale followed the Battle of the Bridges, as it was called by Mildred Lady, Hart Dyke (see page 49).

In 1977, the 140-acre Ridge Farm, Shoreham, which adjoined Castle Farm at the top of the hill towards Well Hill, was up for sale. Once again, with it being adjacent to land we already owned and with 'the boys' showing an increasing interest in farming, we bought Ridge Farm. The buildings were quite substantial, being all built post-war, although they included a few Army Nissen huts. and there was a dairy herd of 90 cows. John Waddilove, who was farming the land, decided to move lock, stock and barrel to another farm away down in Devon. His father, who had been the Duke of Windsor's land agent, had acquired this land and obtained planning permission to erect a full set of buildings to start a dairy herd, and to build a bungalow. We decided against starting a new dairy herd on the farm and in due course converted the buildings for grain storage and our flower-drying enterprise.

During the earlier years of our farming expansion, between 1930 and 1950, we needed to employ an ever-increasing number of workers. They lived either in the farm cottages or in houses we owned in the villages. When the opportunity arose we bought houses, and at the peak of our employment of forty regular workers, we owned thirty-three houses. Many were, of course, occupied by sitting tenants, but there were always some available to house the farm workers. In the long term these property purchases were a good investment as their value increased with keeping them in good repair and they were a realizable asset.

In the post-war years, we also deemed it necessary to have additional houses on some of the farms for the key workers, and we built eight new houses between 1955 and 1973. We were employing first-class herdsmen for the Eynsford herd of Friesian cows. Les Puxty occupied the new house at Manor Farm in 1955, and Neville Free, at Castle Farm, moved in 1957 to one of a pair of semi-detached houses built there, whilst the other house was occupied by the Hewitt family who were also key workers of long standing, particularly in the hop-growing enterprise. A similar pair of semi-detached houses was built at Furlongs Farm in 1953. One was lived in by Jack Turner, the fruit and grain store foreman, and the other by the person in charge of the young stock kept in the cattle yards nearby.

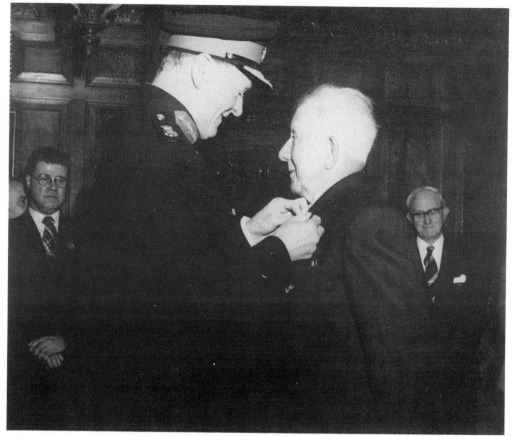

Jack Turner receives British Empire Medal from Lord Astor, 1975 New Year's Honours.

Jack Turner was awarded the British Empire Medal in the 1975 New Year Honours. The citation said: "He had exercised his skill and long experience without thought of reward except the satisfaction of a job well done." During the 58 years that he worked for three generations of the Alexanders, he had related his experiences to many hundreds of visitors and had given valuable advice to the Ministry of Agriculture in their crop trials. He was never happier than when talking to people in the grain store – 'his grain store'. "I knew the time when this place was a little tributary of corn, now its a vast river" he used to say. "It was a trickle, now it's a flood."

We have a very loyal staff of farm workers and perhaps the best illustration of this is the photograph taken at the Kent Show in July 1977 when eight of our older employees, with an average age of sixty-five, were presented with Long Service Awards by Lord Cornwallis, the Lord-Lieutenant of Kent. Their years of service ranged from twenty-seven to sixty-one years and averaged forty-one years. We were employing a regular staff of thirty-three men and women at that time. By 1985 a further eleven employees had also received Long Service Awards.

In 1962 we set up a Pension Scheme, probably one of the earlier farmers to do so, and many of the now retired employees are benefiting from it. Unavoidably, it takes time to build up a pension fund but we know that our employees are pleased to be partaking in the scheme, which will give an additional pension over and above the government scheme. There is also a death-in-service and a widow's benefit incorporated into our scheme.

Long service awards Kent Show, 1977. Lord Cornwallis third from left.

Years of service	Back row LH to RH
REG HEWITT	*DAVID HEWITT*
38	27

Front row LH to RH

ERIC WATTS	JACK TURNER	LES BASHFORD	CHESTER ROBSHAW	FRANK GROOMBRIDGE	NEVILLE FREE
52	61	33	29	56	30

Mary Alexander, with Queen's Silver Jubilee Medal, sketched every calf for pedigree registration with the British Friesian Cattle Society from 1922 to 1977.

The seventh of June 1977 was the Queen's Silver Jubilee, and on the following day
the postman delivered a small registered package addressed to Mrs William Alexander at Home Farm. Our mother was exceedingly surprised upon opening it to learn
that she was one of the recipients of the Queen's Silver Jubilee Medals which were
awarded to persons who had given outstanding service to their country during Her
Majesty's reign. She was then eighty-eight years old and had given all her life to
farming matters and had willingly entertained countless visitors to the farm from
home and many from abroad.

James and I were not without a surprise too that year when at the Kent Show in July
we were very honoured to receive a joint award for our services to dairy farming and
were presented with the Kent Agricultural Society's Queen's Silver Jubilee Medal.

*James and William Alexander receive joint award Queen's Silver Jubilee Medal at the Kent
Show.*

CHAPTER 16
The New Enterprises 1965–72

Eynsford Nurseries

The Nurseries, which we acquired in August 1965, was a completely new venture within our farming business. In order to gain some basic knowledge of the glasshouse industry, we attended several of the Agriculture Ministry's National Agricultural Advisory Service (NAAS) nursery demonstrations and talks, much to the surprise of the professional nurserymen and growers. We obtained very valuable guidance from subsequent discussions with the NAAS officers.

From the very start of our nursery business, we were fortunate to continue employing the existing staff, in particular Jack Clinch, who had also worked for Mr Hutt when he owned nurseries at Swanley. After considerable thought on whom to employ as a manager for the nursery, James and I decided it should be one or our existing employees. John Couchman, who was in charge of the calf rearing and stock management at Dunstall Farm, also had a good knowledge of glasshouse work so it was he whom we chose as manager and he moved into the bungalow at the nursery.

At the date of our purchase there were one and a half acres of chrysanthemums growing in the open ground, and as they were ready for cutting and marketing we very soon became familiar with that business. In the half-acre Venlo-type glasshouses, there were tomatoes being picked, some beds of various flowers, and a section with bloom chrysanthemums being grown for marketing from November to Christmas. In the spring bedding-out plants were grown in large quantities and sweet-scented stocks for cutting. This sequence of cropping gave labour peaks which did not suit our style of management, so we researched the market requirements and found that AYR (All the Year Round) chrysanthemums had a steady demand and would require a level input of labour. We therefore gradually changed to their production and also grew a few beds of carnations and benches of 'Potmums' (chrysanthemums in pots).

Three crops a year of AYR chrysanths were grown from rooted cuttings. We imported, on a weekly basis, over 300,000 cuttings annually from Sardinia which had a suitable climate all year for raising them. The growing of AYRs requires a rigid 'day-length' control system to maintain planting sequence. Every evening, during the longer daylight hours from late spring to early autumn, black polythene sheets were pulled over a wire structure over the growing beds and pulled off again in the morning. To extend the winter day-length numerous 150-watt electric light bulbs above the flower beds were switched on by a time-clock for a set time during the cheap off-peak electricity period. The winter heating of the glasshouses was provided by a 1.5 million BTU oil-fired boiler which circulated hot water through 2-inch pipes running at ground level round all the flower beds.

Eynsford Nurseries All the Year Round Chrysanthemums, 1966.

These requirements were essential to give the plant growth and bud and bloom development the right conditions to meet the tight schedule for the next planting. The AYRs found a very ready market and we found we had been quite competent in tackling the engineering and construction work associated with this new set-up.

Our next involvement in this area was Swanley Flowers Ltd, of which we were founder directors. This was a grower-owned marketing co-operative, formed in September 1971. Our 52-week-a-year production of AYRs was a valuable asset in supplying flowers for the daily van deliveries to florists, this meant we were able to obtain a higher net home price. The involvement of Vic Ross, Chairman, and Janet Horsfall, Secretary, in Swanley Flowers Ltd was invaluable.

The demand for AYRs was in excess of our production capacity and in 1973 we erected an additional three-fifths of an acre of modern glasshouses. In these we were able to incorporate the development of an automatic blackout system and thermo-static ridge-opening ventilation. We also installed a new and more efficient 2.75 million BTU boiler. The new glasshouses gave much better light transmission, which resulted in improved growing conditions and a higher-quality flower to market. We constructed an overhead rail on which a battery-operated unmanned trolley conveyed the cut flowers from the new glasshouses direct to the packhouse. This substantially reduced the walking time.

The ideas incorporated into the new glasshouses allowed the existing labour force of three people to cope with a production increase to 500,000 rooted cuttings a year. These improvements reduced the unit labour costs. A major growing cost during the winter months, however, was the price of the gas oil used for heating. During the mid-1970s, there was a substantial increase in the price of gas oil and we could foresee that because of this, the growing of AYRs was likely to become less viable. This would therefore necessitate a change to growing plants and flowers that were not so

Manor Farm cows walking up Farningham High Street.

dependent upon high temperatures during the winter. We considered the management implications of such a change and reluctantly made the decision in 1976 to sell the nursery. Following this sale we bought the 140-acre Ridge Farm at Shoreham.

Hulberry Dairy Unit

In 1968 we started to consider what improvements could be made to the housing and milking system of pipeline milking and bulk milk tanks which had been installed in 1962 for the 180 cows housed in four cowsheds: 60 in one, 45 in two, and 30 in the fourth. Loose or cubicle housing and parlour milking were in vogue at that time and required far less labour input than our cowsheds. All our units were close to the river Darent and there was restricted building space available for any expansion, so this option at the existing locations was a non-starter.

We had in-depth consultations with the Ministry's NAAS officers and with the help of their computer, it was seen that the most economical use of labour and an overall benefit would be achieved by increasing the herd size, with home-bred heifers by one third to 240 cows and, with careful planning, we would be able to reduce our labour by one third. This would achieve the improvements we were seeking on the cows-per-man objective.

The need to build a completely new dairy unit caused us some heart-searching. However, we knew that one cannot make progress by standing still. Dairying at Manor Farm would become non-viable because of the projected M20 motorway which would

The opening of Hulberry Farm Cowtel, 7th November 1972.

bisect the farm. New Barn Farm, with only thirty cows, was now outdated. So during 1969 we visited many large dairy units to familiarize ourselves with the advantages of these large units and to hear of some of the problems, not least of which was dealing with the huge volume of slurry from cubicle housing systems.

The next year was dedicated to designing a layout that would best suit all our requirements. Cubicle housing, feeding passages, collecting yard, milking parlour, AI cubicles, bull loose box and pen, calving boxes, calf pens, food store, water supply tanks, vacuum pumps, bulk milk tank and compressors, office, telephone, toilet, sundries store, slurry handling and silage clamps. The list was quite formidable but we managed a workable layout.

Hulberry Farm was chosen as the most suitable site. There were 240 acres of land available in one block with a private tarmac road running right through the centre. The mains water and electricity supply were already there. Planning permission was required to build the 'Cowtel' (its adopted name). This was granted, after site meetings with the planning authorities when the reasons for the siting were explained. Permission was also granted for the building of three bungalows in which to house the Cowtel staff.

We made considerable progress in 1970 towards our target date. The point of no return was in the early summer of 1971, when we started placing firm orders for buildings and dairy equipment. For the planning permission application we had employed an architect to draw the plans, but thereafter James and I supervised the whole of the building work and the installations.

We were quite determined to employ our own staff as far as possible. They were keen to be involved in the whole project and they were most adaptable. Much of the annual farm maintenance was postponed for a time—a case of make do but don't mend (within reason).

There was a vast area of concrete to be laid and we opted to mix our own. In order to be conversant with the latest techniques, I attended a three-day concreting course in February at the Cement and Concrete Association's premises at Slough. This was certainly most worthwhile and gave us additional confidence in the work we were about to tackle. Subsequent to the course, we purchased a very large second-hand batch concrete mixer for £75, a second-hand dumper truck for £120, a vibrating screed and levelling board, a concrete poker and rails and panels used as formers. We were then well equipped for the 1,600 tons of concrete that we eventually laid at the Cowtel. We took great care to establish the datum level, and used a Cowley Level throughout the whole project to fix the heights. We found it most satisfying to make all the decisions ourselves.

The building construction started on 8 November 1971. Milking started on 7 November 1972, on time, as planned, exactly one year later. We had not of course finished all the work but were ready to house and milk the cows. The newly established grass fields were to be fenced and the water laid on. And the silage clamp construction was continuing.

It was an historic time when the cows left their old cowsheds. The Manor Farm herd had the most spectacular move to the Cowtel, walking up Farningham High Street, past the shops on both sides and along Sparepenny Lane before going under the railway viaduct and up the hill to their brand-new living quarters at Hulberry Farm. The other three herds, at Home Farm, Castle Farm and New Barn, had a more leisurely walk. The cows were not very content for a while—I suppose, just like people moving house, cows need time to settle in—but in due course all was going like clockwork.

We celebrated the opening of the Cowtel, with all our employees assembling there in the collecting yard. Our uncle, Jack Steven, from Westerham gave a speech of

The carousel milking parlour.

welcome and congratulations to everyone assembled. This was followed by our mother, then eighty-four hoisting the Union Jack. The toast with champagne and refreshments was warmly received by everyone.

The appearance of a new set of buildings on the horizon, and visible from houses in Eynsford village, caused some concern among many of the residents. We had planted several hundred trees as part of a landscaping plan but they don't grow big overnight. On the other hand, people did enjoy seeing the cows grazing the pastures in the spring. We held 'open days' during the year when the locals could come to see the cows at the Cowtel being milked in the 'Carousel' milking parlour, around which we had placed a viewing area, and to see the calves in their individual pens. Seeing was believing.

The Vacated Cowsheds

The increase in the number of cows from 180 to 240 led to more calves to rear, and the empty cowsheds provided the additional accommodation that would be needed. This was part of our overall plan.

Home Farm's two cowsheds were very suitable to adapt to calf rearing. The buildings had excellent ventilation and a large volume of air per calf housed. This contributed to a low relative humidity—an essential factor in rearing healthy calves. The calves were moved from Hulberry to Home Farm when seven days old, having received their dam's colostrum. Neville Free, who had been herdsman at Castle Farm for twenty-six years, semi-retired after the cows left and moved to Home Farm to rear the calves. We had decided to start a once-a-day-only feeding system, about which he was very sceptical. However, after a little while he became an advocate of it. The calves are transferred to Dunstall Farm at the age of seven weeks to continue their rearing. Neville is an excellent calf rearer, having always had a good stockman's eye, and now, at the age of eighty-four, he still enjoys the rearing. At the 1987 Dairy Event at Stoneleigh, Neville Free was presented with the British Friesian Cattle Society's Distinguished Service Award by Mr David Cleveland, the Society's President. He had given over forty years' service with the Eynsford herd. A very notable achievement richly deserved and an award of which he was extremely proud.

Castle Farm cowshed was converted to open yards for accommodating the increased number of steers which were reared through to finished beef at about 20–24 months of age. In the conversion we were able to provide the facility to feed silage mechanically.

New Barn Farm, which had had a small herd of thirty cows, did not lend itself to a conversion to suit our needs. We therefore sold the cottage and farm buildings, together with a small acreage of land. The river meadow was retained for summer grazing.

Manor Farm had the tithe barn as a single-sided cowshed and it was not at all suitable to convert to loose housing. It has very thick walls built of flint and is a listed building. It remained empty for a time.

Loading hop bines for the picking machine.

In-Bin Hop Drying

The hop picking machine which was installed in 1960 was proving very satisfactory. We had made improvements annually to produce a better sample with less labour and to increase its capacity. It was therefore decided in 1967 to expand. The existing oast houses could not take an increased capacity and were not suitable to modernize, so we decided to replace them with an in-bin drying system on a one floor level building. We

In-bin Hop drying.

Mike Stepney and William Alexander with cups won, 1980.

incorporated into the design a completely new cooling system for the hops once they were dried. This was a facility to blow air of a controlled humidity through the hops whilst they were still in the drying bin. They were cooled down in under one hour ready for pressing into the hop pockets. The traditional method of cooling hops on

Tall pylon replaces low old one for new hop garden.

the oast floor takes in excess of six hours and is very much dependant upon the time and cooling space available.

In the first year of drying we lost a lot of sweat and sleep, which is not unexpected with such a pioneering venture. Nevertheless our determination to produce a good sample of hops was amply rewarded when we won the Challenge Cup at the Weald of Kent Ploughing Match hop competition for the best dried sample—of which there were close on 200. We are pleased to say that we have continued to have success in the hop competition there and elsewhere.

In 1971, our farm was one of six selected by the Hops Marketing Board to carry out trials to grow hops seedless—instead of seeded as they all were in the U.K. Nearly all foreign hops are produced seedless and in order to be competitive within the EEC we needed to produce a seedless sample. We changed some unsuitable varieties such as Fuggle which were not viable and have remained seedless ever since. One of the economies was that seedless hops were less bulky and we could therefore dry an increased acreage. We have a very limited acreage of soil suitable for growing hops and there was only one remaining field available. This field had electricity power lines on pylons going across it and their wires would have been too low to give a safety factor above the sixteen-foot high wirework to be erected. To overcome this problem we eventually negotiated a practical solution which involved the electricity company replacing their short pylon with a taller one. The photograph shows this happening before the wirework was erected and the field planted with hop sets in the spring of 1984.

Sevenoaks Grassland Group and Five Farmers

New ideas are continually being developed in every industry. Farmers, however, are perhaps considered unusual in their willingness to show other farmers their achievements.

The acreage of grass grown in the UK is larger than any other crop, and the improved production methods and the better utilization of grass have always been foremost in research. The Sevenoaks Grassland Group was formed in 1960 with a membership of twelve farmers. The idea was to give members the opportunity to see how 'the others' were doing. The initial visits were to each other's farms, where we made a critical analysis of the methods being used and the resultant production. We all benefited greatly from these visits and the ensuing discussions. In due, course visits were arranged to Ministry of Agriculture and commercial experimental farms as well as the luscious grazing pastures in Holland.

During the early 1970s the government was urging farmers to take a closer look at the marketing of their products, and obviously there was a potential to do so with milk. The production of cheese, butter, cream, skim milk, yoghurt, cottage cheese and ice-cream were some options from milk. Five members of our Grassland Group, Messrs A. T. Howie, W. S. Montgomerie, C. M. R. Stoneham, J. R. Alexander and myself, decided to explore the opportunities and we visited several farmers who were producing some of these products. There was undoubtedly a growing demand especially for yoghurt. We eventually decided to go ahead with the idea and formed a company, Garden of England Produce Ltd, in 1972. We traded under the name of Five Farmers, reflecting a farming image. The premises which we chose for the

Five farmers and manager outside office.

Refrigerated delivery vehicles.

operation were the vacant buildings at Manor Farm, which were considered suitable to convert and would still be used for an agricultural purpose, in line with the Ministry's philosophy. We constructed the necessary interior alterations without affecting the outward appearance of the listed tithe barn.

It was not easy launching a new product onto the market but we were successful in doing so and produced a very good variety of fruit-flavoured yoghurts in attractively designed Five Farmers cartons. We provided our customers with a first-class delivery service in smart-looking Five Farmers refrigerated delivery vans.

Apart from our own delivery van sales to shops and other outlets, we negotiated a substantial contract with a large dairy-products company, and supplied a wide range of our products in their own-label containers. Business was really flourishing. We were also producing various flavoured mousses, cottage cheese and ice-cream, all of which gave our vans a good selection of dairy products to deliver to the shops.

It was a sad day for us when the company decided to centralize their production and despatch points, and withdrew from their contracts. It was some time later that Five Farmers decided to cease business and once again Manor Farm buildings became vacant. Our next hope of utilizing the tithe barn was for the conversion to residential use.

CHAPTER 17
Notable events

Vehicles

Jeeps

The excitement of owning an ex-Army USA Jeep prompted Bob Steven, my brother, James, and I to attend a sale of various Army vehicles at Tewkesbury in Gloucestershire in 1947. We bought ten jeeps at prices ranging from £80 to £120. We drove home with five jeeps between us by towing and a piggy back method. We were quite oblivious to the fact that we should not have taken a short cut by motoring through Hyde Park, linked up as we were. We sold six of the jeeps, which paid for the four we kept! A 4-wheel drive vehicle—go anywhere—was quite a luxury, but the open-air travel in winter was anything but a luxury.

Bomb Trolleys
Another buy was six bomb trolleys at an aerodrome in Bedfordshire. They had two axles and a long T-shaped backbone. The 18 × 7 rubber-tyred wheels were exactly what we needed for some low-loading trailers we were building at that time. Also, the concrete mixer handled much more easily on rubber-tyred wheels than on the existing iron wheels.

Horse Shoes
The last account we had for shoeing a farm horse, from Thomas Wood of Swanley, was in 1945, the cost of four shoes being 14 shillings. The dominance of tractors dictated that trailers, and other equipment where practical, needed rubber-tyred wheels.

Livestock

Rabbits
Farmers always have to keep a watchful eye for rabbits, and we erected many miles of rabbit-proof wire-netting fences around fields, particularly those next to rough areas, woodlands and railway embankments or cuttings. During the war rabbit-clearance societies were formed with Ministry backing. This certainly helped to keep the rabbit population down to reasonable levels. Myxomatosis, a viral disease of rabbits, became widespread in about 1953 and wiped out millions of rabbits in a few years. Nature has

a habit of catching up and by 1990 there was growing alarm about the rapid increase of rabbits once again. Set-aside and rough fields favour their existence.

Foot and Mouth

The most worrying time we experienced with a cattle disease was in late October 1967 when a foot and mouth epidemic started in Shropshire. The announcement of that dreaded disease put every farmer on the alert. The very rapid spread of this outbreak was so alarming that country-wide control measures were taken immediately. We barricaded every entrance to our livestock farms and ceased any movement of cattle. The number of daily outbreaks of foot and mouth reached the peak of 81 on 24 November, after which it slowly tailed off by the end of December. The police co-operated magnificently with our provision of warning signs and disinfectant straw mats for vehicle wheels on the A20 and the Dartford Tunnel approach roads. There was a total of 1,974 outbreaks of the disease which resulted in the slaughter of 320,132 animals—cattle, sheep, pigs and goats. Footpaths were closed. Farmers' meetings were cancelled.

Brucellosis

In October 1967, the Ministry of Agriculture, Fisheries and Food launched a Brucellosis Eradication Scheme. We had already been testing our cattle for several years and were very proud to have our four herds included in the first seven herds in England, Scotland and Wales to be accepted into the Scheme.

AI Groups

Artificial insemination (AI) gained impetus following the importation of Friesian bulls from Holland in 1950, and was administered from AI companies. In October 1963, Selective Friesian Services Ltd was launched by the owners of the seven herds Eynsford, Fintalex, Fintdave, Horwood, Hungerford, Plurenden and Whitsbury. Semen was sold from their own home-bred bulls to other herd owners. In due course the choice of semen was extended by SFS purchasing proven and unproven bulls from other breeders. SFS operated through Hampshire Cattle Breeders AI Station.

Another private breeders' AI company, Cattle Breeders Services Ltd, was launched in 1961. The two companies amalgamated in 1982 and traded under the name of Premier Breeders Ltd. They were instrumental in starting the MOET scheme (multiple ovulation embryo transfer) which became foremost in the breeding of 'élite cows'.

Milking Parlour

New designs and ideas are continually being incorporated into milking parlours, which unlike other farm equipment are used twice a day, every day of the year. The Fullwood Rotary Carousel at Hulberry Farm had operated well for nine years and in 1981 the milking parlour was reconstructed. A 16/16 herringbone parlour was installed with the latest electronic equipment comprising automatic cluster removal, milk-flow meters, and computer-controlled concentrate in parlour feeding, which was activated by a transponder attached to each cow's plastic neck collar. The information is fed into the computer in the dairy office. This gives print-outs of milk yields, feed consumed, and breeding information. The electronic equipment is of great assistance to the herdsman at milking time and in monitoring cow performance.

Milk Quotas

By 1984 the production of milk and milk products within the EEC had increased to

New milking parlour with electronic equipment, 1981.

far in excess of the Community's requirements and milk quotas were suddenly brought in overnight to all member countries. This dramatic decision had a devastating effect on many herds, especially those where herd expansion had been made or was in the process of being made. The effect at Hulberry Farm was a reduction in cow numbers to 130. The excess grass acreage was initially used to make more silage, and ultimately the whole grazing pattern and cropping rotation was changed. Farmers are very adaptable to change but overnight bombshells are not easily dealt with.

Weather

Wind

Strong winds and heavy rain were instrumental in blowing down many hop gardens in August 1955, a time of year when the hop bines are becoming very thick and heavy. We unfortunately had 50 per cent of our acreage blown over. We salvaged a large proportion by propping up the wirework with poles and successfully managed to hand-pick many of the hops. The work that winter was concentrated on erecting new poles and wires.

Frost

The very severe and prolonged cold weather in January 1963 will be remembered quite clearly by those people living in Eynsford. The river Darent froze over completely and it became quite safe to drive a car across the frozen ford at Eynsford bridge—we tested it first with a tractor!

The Alexander family actually walked on ice from Eynsford Paper Mill upstream all

River Darent frozen over at Eynsford bridge, January 1963.

the way to Castle Farm. Tractors were often unwilling to start because of frozen fuel lines. Water pipes, both above and below ground, gave tremendous problems and underground pipes in many instances took several weeks to thaw out.

Rain

On 16 September 1968 we had torrential rain, preceded by a frightening spell of thunder and lightning. Two and a half inches of rain fell in a very short period, with a total of 4¼ inches in 14 hours. There was very widespread flooding in the south-east and in Eynsford there was the highest recorded flood level for 128 years. The river Darent became a torrent and flooded fields on both sides. Many bridges were unable to stand the force of the rapid current. Part of one arch of Castle Farm bridge collapsed, and a short distance down the valley, bridges at Lullingstone Castle, New Barn Farm and the Metropolitan Water Board next to the railway viaduct, all totally collapsed and lay in the river bed. Water flooded houses, buildings, destroyed fences, gates and roads, lifted sewer manhole covers and washed soil off fields in the direction that gave least resistance.

Hurricane

There was nothing particularly unusual about the evening of Thursday, 15 October 1987. There had been a lot of rain during the day. However, during the night and especially in the early hours of Friday morning, the 16th, the wind speed suddenly increased to a hurricane force of more than 100 miles an hour by 4 a.m. Those persons who were awoken became terrified and bewildered; many thought that the

A Jeep braves the flooded Darent, September 1968.

Hurricane uprooted trees across the Darent, October 1987.

The dried up Darent river, Summer 1976.

world was coming to an end. Those who slept through it were simply amazed at daybreak. The previous severe hurricane in south-east England was the tempest of 1703. The trail of destruction one saw as one walked out into the roads and streets that morning, was unbelievable. Trees that had been growing graciously for over a hundred years had been blown over like saplings. An estimated 15 million trees were blown down. The town of Sevenoaks received international attention on television, radio and in newspapers: six of its famous seven oaks were uprooted, and incalculable damage had been done to historic buildings in the area.

Fruit trees young and old were also among the casualties. The damage to buildings was unquantifiable. In most places there was no electricity or telephone communication, no trains ran as trees lay across the railway lines, and every road was blocked. It was not long after people became aware of the extent of the damage on that morning of 16 October, that the stillness which followed the storm was broken by the roar of chain-saws which miraculously appeared from nowhere to cut up the fallen trees.

Electricity repair gangs were brought in from as far away as Scotland, Wales and Ireland to repair and in many cases to replace broken lines. Contractors and the Army with big tackle came and cleared the heavy trees. The hurricane left a scar on the countryside that will not be healed in living memory.

Dutch Elm Disease

The country had had a tree disaster occur in 1972, too, when Dutch elm disease spread across the land, eventually destroying an estimated 9 million trees. It denuded many spectacular country lanes, amongst which were Lullingstone Lane and Sparepenny Lane, connecting Eynsford and Farningham. We had to fell many hundreds of dead and dying elm trees, which was a very costly operation, and new fences had to be erected. When one walked along these two lanes it was like being in an empty house without a roof. The beauty of the trees lapping each other overhead had gone.

The hay barn well alight, September 1960.

Drought

We suffered a very severe drought during the summer of 1976 when the temperature in the shade soared to 95 degrees Fahrenheit towards the end of June. Less than 2 inches of rain fell in the three months of June, July and August. The river Darent in Eynsford and beyond completely dried up. The water supply to Hulberry Farm and private residences on the Lullingstone Estate came from a bore hole at Lullingstone Castle, and there was the possibility of this drying up. As a precaution, we bought a 2,000-gallon ex-fuel tank which was thoroughly cleaned out and was then available to take water anywhere. Cattle in the meadows by the dried-up river Darent had water carted to them daily. The pastures everywhere were as bare as a desert and all livestock were fed on the winter store of hay and silage. Our yields of cereals, fruit and hops suffered badly. Rain did not come until September when it fell in abundance, with 4 inches in each of the next four months.

A repeat of the 1976 situation occurred in 1990 when the river Darent went dry from 28 June and did not begin to flow again until towards the end of October. The highest temperature of 95 degrees Fahrenheit was recorded several times during the first weekend of August. A ban on the use of hosepipes for gardens and car washing was in force from early in the spring in many areas of southern England.

Farm Fires

We have unfortunately suffered from many farm fires. Fields of corn were regularly set alight at harvest time when the railway steam engine drivers began stoking up their boilers which caused sparks to fly from the funnel as they passed by the ripening corn. Hay, corn and straw stacks in fields and latterly bales of hay and straw in Dutch barns have always been a hazardous fire risk. In most instances the causes of the fires have remained unknown. The photograph taken in September 1960 shows bales of hay burning fiercely in the Dutch barn at Castle Farm before the fire engines were able to arrive.

CHAPTER 18
Host days

We have been hosts on our farms for very many years to groups of farmers, young farmers' clubs, school parties and to many visitors from abroad. We are only eighteen miles from Marble Arch, the centre of London, so it's a convenient venue, and it has the added attraction of being a mixed farm with a wide scope of activities. My father loved talking to groups of farmers, who listened intently to him at meetings when he would often add, 'Well, if you don't believe what I am telling you, come and I will show you.' And they came, and many of them came again.

In September 1941, during the war, Lord Hudson, then Minister of Agriculture, came to Home Farm and addressed a large gathering of farmers and land owners about the increasing importance of maximizing the production of food from the land. There is a photograph showing him speaking from a farm trailer decorated with our own produce—bottles of milk, two-pound bags of Savoy seed, sheaves of corn, and baskets of apples and pears. Two hop bines growing in the garden can be seen as a background. They acted as a barometer to monitor the growth of hops at Castle Farm two miles away. Also on the trailer are my father, Lord Cornwallis and a government official.

Lord Hudson addressing farmers at Home Farm.

We were very honoured in October 1948 by a visit from the Emir of Abuja of Nigeria and, in May 1949, by a visit from Governor Dewey of New York; in July 1961, Prince Daud, the Prime Minister of Afghanistan, was very interested to see and hear about the different crops which we were growing and to inspect a dairy herd of cows being milked by machine. On all the occasions our mother was happy to provide a Scottish tea.

Open Day

The National Agricultural Advisory Service (NAAS) and the Agricultural Land Service organized an Open Day on all our farms. This was called 'Kent Farmers Field Day' and was held on Wednesday, 29 June 1966. James and I were involved for about a day each week for six months in planning and preparing for the event. There were 35 demonstration points. More than one thousand farmers and advisers attended the day. The assembly point was at Castle Farm where a fleet of lorries, many newly painted, were kindly supplied by Mr N. K. Denham of Wm Lillico & Son Ltd and other corn merchants. The lorries provided a continuous transport service to the nine mount and dismount points. The subjects of the demonstrations at four farms are as listed below.

W. Lillico lorries ready for the off.

Dunstall Farm

1 Calf and young stock rearing. Grazing methods.
2 Building: up and down shed, MAF cattle yard, pole barn for straw.
3 Field beans: varieties and growing techniques.
4 Lucerne crop: Eynsford variety, effects of acid soils.
5 NIAB Barley variety trials.
6 Potatoes: weed control and cultivations on chalkland soil.

Home Farm

1 Lucerne crop: Eynsford variety growing on alkaline soil.
2 Peas for harvesting dry; weed control.
3 Winter and spring wheat: demonstrations and discussion of varieties.
4 Grass seed production: inspect crop of S321 perennial ryegrass.
5 Bulk fertilizer: demonstration unloading 15-ton lorry-load in adapted 15-foot Dutch barn bays.
6 Grain store:
   on-floor and silo-ventilated storage and drying
   seed cleaning and powder dressing machines
   indented cylinders for grass seed cleaning
   bulk bin loading of grain lorries
   milling, mixing and cubing cattle foods.
7 Cattle yards: simple home construction, well ventilated and wind proof.
8 Farm workshop
   newly constructed, insulated roof with roof lights
   winter heating facilities
   thoughtful workshop layout with strong workbench and secure vices
   record-keeping file
   label system for re-ordering machinery spare parts.

Eynsford Nurseries

1 Production of AYR chrysanthemums with day-length control system, packing and marketing.
2 Stocks: flowers for cutting.
3 Outdoor chrysanthemums: one-acre production.
4 Plans: 3½ million BTU boilerhouse.

Castle Farm

1 Friesian cows:
   inspection of pedigree herd
   grazing management
   high tensile wire fencing
   inspection of cowshed and bull pen.
2 Grass conservation: barn hay drying, silage clamp.
3 Savoys: Alexander's No. 1 Savoy seed production at pod setting stage of growth.
4 Apple orchard: land drainage demonstration. Four-foot deep hole dug to show root penetration and worm activity and where a compact layer of soil affects growth.
5 Hops:
   viewing of hop garden from road only (wilt precaution)
   exhibit of plans to modernize the complete drying system for next years' crop with bulk-loading of 8-foot square bins for a progressive three-stage drying process and a controlled humidity cooling system allowing hops to be pressed into hop pockets one hour later.
6 Concrete: concrete-laying demonstration by the Cement and Concrete Association using vibrating tamper-screed boards.

7 Meteorology: the weather men from Bracknell had a display to show how weather forecasts and services could be used to benefit farmers.

8 Bookstall: the Ministry of Agriculture had a bookstall with free and for sale publications.

9 Pye Tele-communications provided walkie-talkie facilities to the 'stations' and demonstrated their uses in farming.

10 Buffet and Bar refreshments were available.

11 Histographs: exhibited showing gross margins on Land, Labour and Capital. Also labour peaks and troughs relative to the large and varied number of farm enterprises.

12 Office records: we showed a card system we were using which gave tractor drivers details of fertiliser application, crop drilling and crop spraying rates. All fields had names and numbers. The completed details from these cards were entered in a cropping book which has been kept continuously since James and I started entries in 1942. Simple and effective recording.

The Open Day was regarded as highly successful by the organizers and was very much appreciated by the visiting farmers. The opportunity to see how fellow farmers are operating is always worth a day away from home. We were more than thankful to have been blessed with a fine sunny day.

One of the memories which many people relate following their visits to our farms, is about the farm workshops. They return home determined to improve their own. A

Open day. Good Farm Management.

Farm workshop.

place for everything and everything in its place probably sums up their remarks. We do not keep any records of tools going in and out of the workshop but there is a place to hang up each one. The workshop motto is 'It takes less time to put things away than it does to look for them'. Such a simple system works. All that is required is to have a place for every item on walls or shelves. An empty place always calls for the return of the absent item. Colour coding of similar tools is used where applicable—for example, to distinguish between whitworth, metric and AF spanners. Coloured waste bins, usually old drums, stand in suitable places to receive waste metal, burnable items, floor sweepings and glass. There is no reason not to use them!

CHAPTER 19
When the boys came home

As the families were growing up, James and Diana, and Marion and I wondered which of them would follow the Alexander tradition and become farmers.

Douglas, our youngest son, decided to take up a career in veterinary medicine. From an early age he had always enjoyed looking after young animals on the farm and later on spent some time with local vets whilst at school in Sevenoaks. After he had passed three A Level exams at Sevenoaks School he studied on a six-year course in veterinary medicine at Gonville and Caius College, Cambridge University from October 1979. He was awarded a degree in Medical Sciences (MA) in 1982. During the next three years he had 26 weeks of practical experience with vets in Kent, Surrey and Lincolnshire. In the summer vacation of 1984 Douglas travelled to New Zealand and gained experience on cattle veterinary work in seven practices. On the completion of his six years in Cambridge, he gained a degree in veterinary medicine (Vet. MB) and was admitted to the Royal College Veterinary Surgeons (MRCVS). Marion and I were very thrilled with his achievement and pleased to be present at the Graduation Ceremony which took place just ten days after we had moved into our new house at Manor Farm. Douglas worked in practices in Kent and Essex before having a six-month working holiday in Australia during 1987. He has a particular interest in small animal orthopaedics and works in a practice based in St Leonards-on-Sea, East Sussex.

My son William and James's two sons James and Robert (in descending order of age) were all prospective farmers. After leaving school each of them gained farming experience in different avenues.

William left Sevenoaks School in 1970 with three A Levels, and worked as a student for one year on Poul Christensen's newly acquired 700-acre rented farm in Berkshire. This had previously been poorly farmed, providing William with valuable experience of how careful management could bring a farm round. He worked very long hours with the dairy cows, their young stock and the arable crops.

In September 1971 he began a three-year degree course at Wye College, part of London University, studying Agricultural Business, which would stand him in good stead later in life. He used his summer vacations to gain practical experience on different enterprises, e.g. pea vining in Essex. At the end of his second year, William had the honour of being presented to the Queen Mother, Chancellor of Wye College, in his capacity as organizer of the Wye College Annual Summer Ball.

He left Wye in 1974 with an honours degree (BSc.) and received the Agricola Prize—awarded to the best all-round student of the year. During the many celebrations which took place before leaving Wye, William met Caroline Keen, whom he later married.

It seemed common practice for students to travel abroad after leaving Wye, and William left for Auckland in New Zealand in July. He found work of his own accord on various farms where seasonal help was required. The dairy farmers have a heavy calving period in July/August and need assistance with milking and feeding calves. Later in the season there was silage and hay making followed by the cereal harvest. Casual farm work was scarce around Christmas time as there was plenty of family help, so William found work on a gas-pipe-laying project—good pay, but a few weeks' work was long enough.

In the north of South Island, the hop-picking season started in February but before working there for three weeks he motored to the very southern end and enjoyed the spectacular scenery and boating on the rapids. Soon after William arrived in Auckland, he bought a car to enable him to move from job to job. His next work was in Tasmania where he gained valuable knowledge during a six-week stay with Harold and Clover Davey on their hop farm, processing and pelleting hops for the export market. When work finished there William travelled to mainland Australia and met up with George Streatfeild, a college colleague. They bought a pick-up truck and toured Central Australia from Adelaide to Darwin and down the eastern coastline to Canberra, where they sold the vehicle before parting company. It was a very thrilling experience for two student friends.

William then travelled 2,000 miles by bus across the Nullarbor Plain to Perth and from there hitchhiked north for the 1,000 miles to the prosperous mining area in Western Australia where work on sheep stations was exchanged for your keep. On the way south he found work on a 10,000-acre farm sowing corn. His work timetable was from 6 p.m. to 8 a.m. for 21 days non-stop. There was good night work pay but no time or place to spend money.

His finances had swollen by this time so he used his earnings to pay for a trip to South America. This adventure started from Bogota, the capital of Colombia, with a group of twelve young students travelling in a mini-bus for 13,000 miles across eight South American countries, camping in such exotic places as the Andes, Lake Titicaca, and Patagonia, finally finishing up at Rio de Janeiro, where he saw in the New Year.

The whole eighteen months away gave William the experience of being an employee, obtaining work, adapting to unusual situations and the need to plan ahead. He had left England as a young student and returned home as a sun-tanned young man.

James left Sutton Valence Boarding School in 1972 and had a year's practical farming at the BOCM—Silcock's 300 dairy cow experimental farm at Knaptoft—where he gained very wide experience. He followed this by studying for an HND (Higher National Diploma in Agriculture) at Seal Hayne College in Devon.

This required a further one year's practical as part of a sandwich course, which was taken after the first year's study, at the Whitsbury Farm in Hampshire, where he worked with arable, dairying and sheep. After obtaining his HND he continued studying for a further year and was awarded a Diploma in Management Studies after which he worked at Home Farm for a year before embarking on a world tour.

The International Agriculture Exchange Association arranges world trips for young farmers requiring experience. James travelled via Thailand, Malaysia and Singapore to Australia where he worked for four months in Southern Victoria on a dairy farm. Organized tours were arranged by the IAEA for their participants to see agriculture and places of interest in other parts of Australia and also in New Zealand, after which James travelled via Fiji and Hawaii to Canada. He worked for seven months on a very extensive farm of 1,280 acres (two square miles) in Alberta where beef rearing and spring-sown cereals were the enterprises.

During the final two weeks of the year's programme, thirty of the students embarked on a whistle-stop tour, by Greyhound buses, of the USA before returning home in November 1979. The opportunity to see and experience farming in so many countries provided James with a very useful farming background.

Robert left Sutton Valence Boarding School in 1973 and spent his first year's practical farming on Mr R. Langmead's dairy and arable farm at Chichester. This was preparatory to a one-year general course at Plumpton Agricultural College where he received a National Certificate in Agriculture in 1975. He followed this by a further year's practical work, mainly with cows but also sheep, at a farm in west Wales, after which he took an advanced NCA course specializing in livestock at Moulton Agricultural College, Northamptonshire.

Robert's trip abroad started in July 1977 and was arranged through the Marvin Relief Agency in New Zealand.

He spent his first six months there milking cows and then had a travelling holiday for two months with a college colleague, visiting places of interest in the North and South Islands. His next arranged work was in Western Australia during their autumn drilling season. But before crossing Australia he purchased an Aussie Coach Pass in Melbourne and enjoyed a sightseeing trip up the east coast and down through central Australia via Ayers Rock to Adelaide before crossing the Nullarbor Plain to Perth—ready for work. It was the time of year for drilling cereal crops and Robert enjoyed work for six weeks in the large fields of between 50 and 200 acres. The huge tractors were 180 hp and pulled a drilling width of 40 feet; the fields or paddocks as they were called were mainly flat.

When Robert left Perth he flew to Katmandu and, with a group of nineteen other young people, travelled in an ex-army truck through Nepal, India, Pakistan, Afghanistan, Iran, Turkey and across Europe back home.

Some of the highlights of the journey were viewing Mount Everest (from a distance), visiting the Taj Mahal at Agra in India, crossing the Khyber Pass from Pakistan into Afghanistan, and visiting Troy and other interesting ancient remains in Greece. The journey in the truck was about 10,000 miles and took eleven weeks. The agriculture in India and Pakistan was very backward with a lot of work being done with oxen and by hand. Where he travelled through Afghanistan there were only sheep and goats grazing the mountainous regions and going across Iran all he saw was desert. Robert certainly had a great travelling experience before settling back in Eynsford.

After returning from their various world tours, William, James and Robert each decided they would like to join in the farming businesses being run by their fathers. They were each allocated special responsibilities in addition to their regular work and in due course my brother James and I were able to take a less active part in the day-to-day running of the farms. Eventually it was considered that it would be appropriate for the two families to farm independently of each other but to use each other's resources as far as was practical. We were all very much aware that this would be a major undertaking requiring extremely careful planning. So from the very start we agreed to take professional advice on all the aspects of this complex reorganization plan. All the intricacies involved were overcome with perseverance and understanding on all sides.

The existing farming company's assets were divided into two new companies each with equal assets and came into being on the first February 1981. The name of

William Alexander (Eynsford) Ltd, registered in 1946, was replaced by J. & R. Alexander (Eynsford) Ltd, and William Alexander (Shoreham) Ltd.

In this manner we retained our previous well-known identity and the farming practices remained much as before but with separate ownerships. Both companies have business with each other and each is able to pursue their farming plans independently. It is more than ten years since we reorganized and the wisdom of that decision has been proved without question.

James and I enjoy and have benefited from being involved in committee work connected with both farming activities and village affairs. The grain store at Furlongs Farm became a very popular venue at which to hold Barn Dances and from 1969 they were a regular bi-annual event for many years. The farm atmosphere was always enhanced by the presence of two young calves penned in the building. They soon became soothed by the music and slept! Dancers brought their own hampers of food and we provided strawberries and cream.

Other fund raising events were also run regularly by Marion and Diana at their homes. They were always able to muster plenty of helpers because of their own enthusiasm. Their afternoon parties, embracing many stalls, particularly good-as-new clothes, were looked forward to every year and were very generously supported.

Marion and Diana also very much enjoyed being in a group of twelve ladies who lived in the village. Every month one of them provided lunch in her own home, so each lady's turn as host only came round once a year—you were a guest for the other eleven lunches! As none of the other ladies' husbands were farmers, they had different topics to discuss about a multitude of subjects and quite naturally village news was forthcoming from everyone. Have you heard that . . . ?

This Ladies Luncheon Group as they are known was started in 1960 and now, just over thirty years later, the group, still continues to flourish and to enjoy each others companionship albeit with some new members to keep the number at twelve.

Two of the village organizations to which James and I contribute most are the Eynsford Village Society, founded in 1945, and the Eynsford Village Hall Trustees (1905). James was chairman of the Village Society from 1969 to 1977 and has been their President since 1986. The society monitors many important aspects which affect village life and environmental issues. I became a trustee committee member of Eynsford Village Hall in 1970 and have been their chairman since 1977. The Hall is used extensively by the many village organizations for their events and functions and is also let to people outside the village. It is self-financing and runs regular fund-raising events. Both of these two organizations contribute greatly to the continuing community life in Eynsford village.

In the farming sphere, James is very involved with National Farmers Union and Milk Marketing Board committee work. At the Kent Show held every July he is the Chief Steward responsible for running the milking dairy which he has done since 1967. The public always show a great interest in seeing cows being milked, whether by machine or, occasionally, by hand. James was elected to Council in 1965 and a Vice-President in 1980.

I belong to several committees connected with hops and became an NFU delegate to the EEC Hops Committee in Brussels in 1974 for twelve years. Their meetings were interesting but so often frustrating. Proposals were debated for new or variations of the Hop Market Regulations. We were there to give opinions but not to make decisions.

I had an absorbing period of twelve years judging farm machinery entered for the RASE Machinery Silver Medal Award Scheme. This entailed farm visits to see the machines at work and to assess their merits, which were discussed with judges from other parts of the country. My judging from 1978 to 1990 was both interesting and educational.

James and I, with other co-judge farmers, judged many farm competitions, particularly in Hampshire. A few days away from home looking over other farms always brought back new ideas and stimulated one's thoughts.

Travelling for pleasure is always an agreeable change from business travel. Flying on Concorde started a new era of fast and luxurious travel. Fun flights became available and Marion and Iris Holbrook, her hairdresser friend, had one such trip in October 1983. They were very thrilled at breaking through the sound barrier and were as full of excitement on leaving the plane as they were on boarding it. Ed Holbrook and I, however, preferred train travel so whilst Marion and Iris were enjoying their flight, we planned a trip on the Orient Express train from London to Venice. The date we chose was the 17 June 1984. James and Diana, together with four other friends in the village, made up a party of ten. Arrangements were made that we should meet at Castle Farm on the evening before our departure. Little did I realize that the 16 June would be such a memorable day in another way.

The Queen's Birthday Honours list was published that morning in the newspapers and I was awarded the OBE. That honour was more than I could ever have dreamed about. Our evening meeting had a double celebration.

The Orient Express train at Victoria Station.

The trip on the Orient Express was simply marvellous and we thoroughly enjoyed unknown comfort in train travel. We stayed three nights in Venice, followed by a very scenic and pleasant train journey through the picturesque Alps to Vienna where we stayed a further three days. Whilst in Venice we enjoyed another celebration – Ed and Iris's 25th wedding anniversary. That evening we were all serenaded in two gondolas from our hotel, along the canals to a decorated restaurant on the water's edge by the Rialto bridge where we enjoyed a delicious meal in such a romantic setting. We flew home by British Airways from Vienna having had a truly memorable week.

I was very thrilled with the flood of letters that awaited me on our return from holiday. The Investiture at Buckingham Palace was held on the 31 July, and I was

William with OBE award and Marion at Buckingham Palace.

accompanied by Marion and our two daughters Mary and Margaret. They viewed the proceedings within the Palace from a seated balcony.

My unforgettable moment was to hear my name announced, to walk forward, bow to the Queen, receive the OBE medal, shake hands and then·be asked a question about farming—it was all over in a few minutes but the memory is for a lifetime. We all had photographs taken in the Palace courtyard, after which we were joined by William and Caroline at the Farmers Club for a celebration lunch.

CHAPTER 20
Two new developments

Two major concerns which were still exercising our minds in 1982, and which were part of the reorganization plans, were the development of Manor Farm buildings and the increasing lack of suitable storage facilities for cereals and other crops in the foreseeable future. The total acreage of combinable crops was gradually increasing and so were the yields per acre. Where two tons per acre of wheat had seemed a respectable yield for many years, we were now able in many instances to achieve three tons and even average it in a good year. The decision was therefore made to build a new grain store at Castle Farm for the Shoreham company; the Eynsford company would then be left with ample facilities themselves.

We adopted the same planning procedure for this major undertaking as we had done for previous ones. One year to look at existing set-ups, one year to plan our own and one year to build. It may seem a long time, but we were looking far enough ahead so as not to be hurried.

After harvesting the 1984 crop of wheat, where the grain store was to be built, the contractors started to erect the main building structure and also the drier which was to be housed within the building. Other contractors installed the 100-ton and 40-tons grain storage bins with all their ancillary equipment. Our own farm staff constructed all the concreting works and block walling. Once more, I was pleased to use my welding skills and build the metal platform for the grain cleaner. The grain store was ready to operate for the 1985 harvest although finishing work continued into the next year. The 42-foot high, 1200-ton grain store is located in the bottom of the valley within a complex of existing farm buildings which meant that a road, electricity and water were available. The building could be viewed from the public roads on both sides of the valley and we paid particular attention to the building design and landscaping features to reduce the public view and to enhance the environmental aspects. Our careful planning was amply rewarded when we won the Country Landowners Association 'Farm Buildings Award' for the South of England in 1987. A cast-iron plaque commemorating the award adorns an outside wall of the building.

Obtaining permission to convert the tithe barn at Manor Farm to living accommodation was a long and tedious business requiring very detailed architectural planning. Permission was eventually granted to divide the tithe barn into four units, each with three or four bedrooms, and the pair of semi-detached farm cottages required the improvement of their external appearance.

Additional planning permission was also granted for a development within the curtilage of the farmyard, comprising two bungalows and a two-storey house.

Our eldest son, William, and Caroline Keen were married in October 1979 and they lived at Lower Austin Lodge farm. Their daughter Lorna was born in July 1982, and Thomas in February 1985. William was responsible for running the day-to-day

New grain store Castle Farm, 1985.

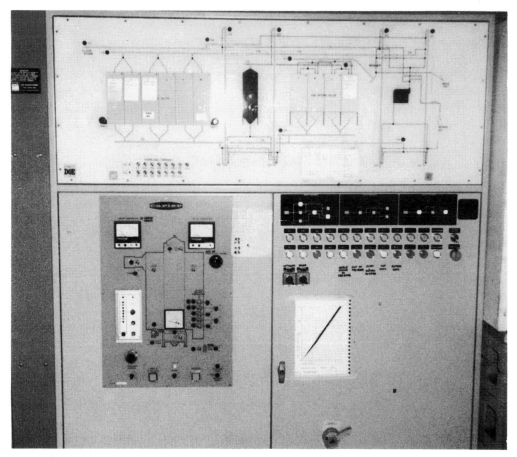

Control panel for grain store equipment.

business at Castle Farm, as well as the other farms of the Shoreham Company. Marion and I realized that it would be prudent for them to occupy Castle Farmhouse and we decided to move to Manor Farm when the new house was built. We therefore became very closely involved with its design and eagerly watched the building of it stage by stage.

It was just coincidence that the building of the grain store at Castle Farm and the house at Manor Farm were both started on the same day, 24 September 1984. The house was completed in early June and we moved in on the 11th. There was a feeling of sadness as we left Castle Farmhouse, having lived there for thirty-four years of our married life and brought up a family of four. William, Caroline and their two children moved into Castle Farm two days later. My work routine changed to mornings only at the farm with the remainder of the day at our new home. A small workshop had been incorporated into the garage/house design and this was a real boon for the DIY work which I very much enjoy. It was not easy to move from a spacious farmhouse to a very much smaller new house. We employed a landscape architect to plan a garden layout as we had a completely bare area of ground around the house, and were very happy creating the new garden. There were eight other properties on the estate, all occupied, and we arranged an 'At Home' welcome to them all five weeks after we moved in.

I find it hard to relate that the saddest day of my life was on 6 August 1985, when Marion suddenly and peacefully died of a heart attack. This was just eight weeks after moving to Manor Farm. It was unbelievable. I felt a sudden vacuum in my life. My family and friends rallied round to give every comfort they could. The funeral service was held in St Martins Church, Eynsford. It was packed to capacity. Marion was no longer with us in person but will always be there in our memories.

Manor Farm house, 1991.

My life was empty for a long while. But I began to count my blessings.

We had moved house.

Douglas had just qualified as a vet and Marion and I had attended his graduation day at Cambridge on 21 June.

Mary was a re-insurance broker in Hamburg and had married Dieter Scholz on 24 May 1984. They lived in the country on the outskirts of Hamburg.

Margaret was a sugar trader in London and had married Robert Miles on 16 May 1981. They lived just north of Peterborough.

We had wedding receptions and celebrations for both girls at Castle Farm. These were events that Marion really enjoyed organizing and at which she excelled.

My thoughts eventually turned to writing a book of the family history and I don't think I could have chosen anything else more interesting and time-consuming. The research it required gave me a good reason to visit people and places and I made many new friends. I travelled to Scotland several times to research the Alexander family background and nearer home became a frequent visitor to the local libraries.

The centenary of the Alexanders' moving to Home Farm would not be until February 1992. In true Alexander fashion I started research and writing soon enough so as not to be hurried. Six years before!

CHAPTER 21
Adjusting in 1986

Christmas is a joyous period when we remember each other with cards and presents and have parties at which we renew acquaintances and meet new people. I was pleased to receive a great many invitations of hospitality. In March 1986, I joined Ed and Iris Holbrook for a week's skiing in Wengen. It was a wonderful holiday and once again I enjoyed the thrills and spills on the snow-covered mountains of the Swiss Alps. Subsequently I renewed a friendship with Diana Le May, whom we as a family had known since the mid-1930s. Her father, Dudley Le May, was a hop factor and he made regular visits for many years to Castle Farm. On several occasions he brought his three daughters, Diana, Jill and Jackie, with him and the families had always kept in touch. Diana was widowed in 1983 and lived alone in Tunbridge Wells. In the spring of 1986 our friendship began to grow and after I returned from an International Hop Congress in Oregon, USA, in August we became engaged and were married in October of that year.

During the war Diana served in the WRNS for four years. In 1948 she went to Nyasaland to spend a year with her mother's cousin, Daisy Woodward whose brother Stuart May lived in Shoreham for many years. Mrs Woodward owned a tea estate and her estate manager was Hans (John) Gruber who had left his native Austria for Africa in 1938. He became a tea planter in 1942. Diana married John in 1949 who, after the war, became a naturalised British subject. Their son Mark was born in 1950 and in 1953 it was decided to return to England. Before doing so, at Diana's father's request, they agreed to change their name by Deed Poll to the family name of Le May so that Mark would carry on the name as Diana had no brother.

Marion and I had always kept in touch with Diana and John. Our daughters had spent some time together at Tonbridge Girls Grammar School. Diana is a very keen gardener and together we have created the garden which Marion and I had planned.

My research and book writing took second place for a while whilst Diana and I were adjusting to our new lives and getting to know each other's families and friends. Diana's son Mark lives in Edinburgh with his wife Maggie and their two children Henry and Mahala. Mark was awarded an honours degree (B.Sc.) in Town and Country Planning at Heriot Watt University. He also has a certificate in Community Education and is manager of Cannon Mills Community Care in Edinburgh. Her daughter Sarah lives in London with her friend Jet who has two daughters. For many years Sarah and Jet have run a refuge for women and their children escaping from violence.

We all have something which we would like to do or try out but never quite make sufficient effort to do so. In September 1987, I achieved one of my ambitions which was to make a parachute jump—perhaps not envied by many people. This ambition was prompted at a wedding I attended when four of the guests came down by parachute and landed with apparent ease on the reception lawn. My enquiries led me to Headcorn Parachute Club one Suday afternoon where I learned that there were two options: either make a solo jump, which required a full day's training, or a tandem jump, which needed only a half-hour's instruction. I chose the latter, having convinced Diana (almost) that it was absolutely safe. I then patiently waited for a good day to jump.

Everything fell into place for 3 p.m. on Thursday 17 September. There was a beautiful clear sky with a slight wind and some sunshine. It was the first really fine day for some time and farmers were taking the opportunity to burn straw. On arrival at Headcorn, I registered with my Tandem Instructor, Jack Gregory, an American. Because I was over forty years of age I had to produce a doctor's certificate saying that I was fit and that he knew of no reason why I should not make a parachute jump. Another stipulation was that I should be under 15 stone in weight. No problem with either! I paid a fee for the instruction and for the jump. This also covered provisional membership of the British Parachute Association. I agreed to hire another parachutist to take photographs of the whole event: he would jump just before us to take some good action photos!

I was wearing lightweight trousers and a summer shirt and I was kitted up with a red one-piece suit which zipped right up the front and around each ankle. A sort of harness was then produced which consisted of very stout straps and buckles, which went round one's waist, over the shoulders and between the legs. It was all tightened up very securely. A soft leather close-fitting hat, close-fitting goggles and gloves completed the outfit. My instructor put on his gear and then we went to the practice box. This simulated the inside of the plane in which we were to fly. He carefully explained the procedure. He sat down on the floor facing the tail of the plane with me sitting between his legs and leaning tightly against his chest. He then fastened two top

Inside the plane.

and two bottom slips of his harness to the respective hoops on the back of my harness. We then shuffled up on to our knees towards the exit opening. He fastened a left- and a right-hand strap from his hips to mine, so we were snugly together. At the opening I sat with my legs dangling over the edge of the fuselage. This was the position to be in at the jump. We repeated this practice a second time to make certain the procedure was understood. We were now ready!

There were eight parachutists jumping; this number made up a plane load. Our names were called out over the loud-speaker system and we all walked out to the plane complete with parachute pack and altimeter instrument. My cameraman took photos of the group before we stepped into the plane's fuselage. It was a Britten Norman Islander twin-engined propeller plane. Four people faced the other four people all sitting on the floor. There was no door to close!

My instructor then fastened me to him as per our practice. The plane taxied across the grass field and the pilot waited for clearance from air traffic control at Gatwick. We soon took off and in moments were airborne. There was a really clear and superb view, looking out of the fuselage opening, to the fields below. We circled higher and higher like going up a spiral staircase, so as to remain within sight of the airfield. The altimeter readings soon crept up to 1,000 feet then 2,000, 3,000 and at 4,000 feet two parachutists were ready to leap out.

The pilot throttled back the engine so that he wasn't climbing and then out they both jumped, just like we would have off a high wall. I looked out moments later and they seemed so far below in only seconds, swinging gently to earth. We climbed further to 5,500 feet and asked for clearance from air traffic control to go up to 10,000 feet. As there were other planes about, the pilot was only allowed to circle to 6,000 feet. At this height two more parachutists leapt out and then it was our turn. We shuffled over to the exit and I sat with my legs dangling over the side. I couldn't fall as

The parachute jump.

I was strapped to my instructor. Strangely enough, I did not feel nervous although the ground did look a long way below. I think it must have been because my ambition was about to become a reality. I was holding my hands tightly round my harness shoulder straps, head back, back arched, all as instructed and with my legs together and ready to bend knees as soon as we jumped. The instructor said 'Three two, one. Jump!' That left you no further time for thoughts! You feel the coolness of the fresh air rushing by as you hurtle down free-fall reaching a speed, I am told, of up to 110mph. The 10 seconds of free fall soon happened for the 1,500–2,000 feet drop.

Then the instructor pulled the ripcord and with a jerk our speed was dramatically reduced. The parachute had opened! We were then able to talk to each other, or rather shout as one's ears had gone pop at the higher altitude. He unfastened the strap tying our bodies together so I was freer to move my legs and arms. It really was a splendid sensation descending relatively slowly. Looking up towards the sky I was so reassured to see the parachute. Looking down to earth the fields seemed to zoom up. The instructor pointed out the marked place where we were to land in the airfield. The parachute was straight-sided and curved. It was larger than usual because there were two persons. By pulling the cord attached to the left side we turned left and similarly the right cord turned us to the right. There were loops on these cords for me to put my hands through so that I could feel the sensation of guiding the parachute down. By pulling both cords together it slowed up the speed of the descent considerably. I could see my wife Diana and two other people gazing up at us and hurrying towards our landing spot. It was already time for quick thinking. 'William, remember the landing technique,' said my instructor. 'Legs together, knees slightly bent and hands gripping shoulder straps.' We were at ground level all too quickly and very near the marked spot. We had made an excellent gentle landing—running along a few paces before stopping and standing quite still. It was very little different from stepping off a moving bus.

I had accomplished an excellent parachute jump with no adverse effects at all. I was so very pleased. Diana was even more pleased to see me on terra firma and to receive a welcome kiss. We all chatted about the jump as we walked back to the undressing room. The instructor presented me with a certificate for my Tandem Descent from 6,000 feet.

Twenty minutes to go up. Four minutes to come down!

CHAPTER 22
Completing the century

T he most outstanding decision affecting British Agriculture in our family's century of farming was the United Kingdom's entry into the Common Market in 1973. The European Economic Community was founded under the Treaty of Rome on 25 March 1957. Before writing about some of the effects on farming once being in the EEC, I would like to relate a few words about another century celebration.

A Festival of British Food and Farming was held in London's Hyde Park from 5 to 7 May 1989. The Ministry of Agriculture, Fisheries and Food were celebrating their first hundred years and the Royal Agriculture Society of England were celebrating their 150 years of existence. Some very striking statistics were given. In 1839 60 per cent of the household income was spent on food compared with 13 per cent today. Then the average citizen had to work for two and a half hours to earn enough money to buy a loaf of bread whereas today it takes only six minutes. Production per worker has increased dramatically and 2½ per cent of today's workforce now produce 60 per cent of Britain's food requirement. The last Exhibition held in Hyde Park (named after Hyde, an ancient manor and hunting ground formerly belonging to Westminster Abbey and first open to the public in 1637) was in 1851. At that time a visitor would have seen a very different capital city. There were orchards and market gardens in Chelsea and Hammersmith and pigs were kept under beds in Kensington. Pig raising was a cottage industry amongst the infamous tenements.

Now, a century and a half later, London and its suburbs have spread south as far as Swanley, which is the junction for the Dartford tunnel under the Thames and also on the famous M25 motorway. Those of us living in the Darent Valley really do appreciate the unspoilt countryside and hope that the M25 ring-road around London will be a protective barrier to urban development and thus allow farming to continue in a reasonable manner.

It has taken some little while since joining the EEC in 1973 for farming to adjust to the various commodity regulations that were in force at that time. The UK is no longer singly able to make its own decisions and the EEC wranglings are very often most extensive.

Forty years ago the economics of farming were a national concern within a world market scene, and during that period British farmers responded magnificently to the encouragements and inducements to adopt new techniques and machinery. It is rather ironical that their productivity grew to such an extent that there was overproduction of certain commodities here and elsewhere within the EEC. These were referred to as grain mountains, butter mountains and wine lakes, to give but three examples.

A savage overnight milk quota was imposed on the dairy industry sector in March

1984. This caused many unpleasant upheavals but in due course stabilized the situation. In the cereal sector co-responsibility levies were implemented, varying annually according to total production. Also in the attempt to reduce the area of cereals grown, an EEC scheme called 'Set-aside' was launched. To qualify, farmers had to reduce their cereal acreage by a minimum of 20 per cent for a period of five years, for which they received an annual payment of £80 per acre. The set-aside area could be fallowed, planted as a woodland or used for non-agricultural purposes, eg. horses.

Environmental issues were having an increasingly vocal lobby and special areas were being designated under the following titles: AONB—Areas of Outstanding Natural Beauty; SSI—Areas of Special Scientific Interest; NSA—Nitrogen Sensitive Areas, ESA—Environmentally Sensitive Areas.

Many normal farming practices were being curtailed or regulated and profit margins were being eroded. The diversification of farming operations was being encouraged in order to supplement incomes. These included the conversion of redundant farm buildings for use as craft workshops and for light industry, farm shops, pick-your-own (PYO) operations, farm trails, tourism, recreational facilities, including golf courses in suitable locations, and Bed & Breakfast accommodation.

James and I have, during the last forty-five years, experienced many changes in farming practices. So we decided that the responsibilities of entering into some of these new diversification schemes should rest squarely on our sons' shoulders.

Our mother, who had lived at Home Farm since she came from Scotland in 1919, had failing health in 1978 and she spent the last few years of her life in the comfort of a nursing home in Sevenoaks, where she died in 1986 at the age of ninety-eight. She had continued to take an interest in the farm 'goings on', but in due course they were beyond her understanding. She was very happy to know that her two grandsons James and Robert had moved from Meadow View into Home Farm house and that it was being well looked after.

In April 1987 James married Sarah Collins; they live at Home Farm. Robert moved to Furlongs Farm, to a house close by the grain store, and married Caroline Brooks in October 1988.

Their sister, Jane, who was National Dairy Queen in 1980 was married in September 1982 to Richard Frankson, and they live in the farmhouse at Hulberry Farm, a little distance beyond the Cowtel.

When a new generation occupies an old house, they so often like to explore behind what the previous generation may have covered up. Home Farm became no exception to this. After the Aga cooker was moved from Gran's kitchen to another downstairs room, the wall behind the cooker was carefully taken away to reveal an inglenook, very extensive, with seating on both sides. It was carefully restored. One could picture the Alexander family, on their arrival from Scotland in February 1892, sitting around this inglenook and enjoying the warmth of a blazing log fire. Home Farm house was one of seven built on the Lullingstone estate by the Hart Dykes between the early and mid-eighteenth century. They all had the distinctive feature of being square in shape and having dormer windows in the roof which sloped down to a flat area in the centre. This was accessible through a small roof door in the attic. Farmhouses were built at Home Farm, Eynsford; Park Gate, Lullingstone Park; Cockerhurst House, Shoreham; Wested Farm, Crockenhill; Petham Court, Swanley; Pedham Place, Swanley, and East Hall, Orpington.

Home Farm house, 1963.

Sarah and James in the inglenook fireplace, Home Farm.

Diversification

The house at Home Farm, which is built on sloping ground, has three storeys with an attic, whereas the other houses were only two storeys with attics. My nephew James and Sarah decided to develop a farmhouse Bed & Breakfast as part of the farm diversification, and with a lot of thought and great determination they adapted rooms to provide three bedrooms with bathrooms en suite. The large farmhouse is fully utilized and very well patronized by guests. Another success has been the letting of disused stables which have had interior alterations and were readily in demand as small unobtrusive workshops situated in the quietness of the countryside.

As another diversification enterprise, William and Caroline looked at the possibility of marketing full-length hop bines. The production of hops was far exceeding the demand by brewers, and growers' prices were at rock bottom. Their initial market research suggested that the demand for fresh green bines was limited, but that real possibilities existed for selling dried hop bines. Special drying techniques and packaging methods were developed to enable the dried bines to be supplied to any location in the country in the best condition for hanging up decoratively—thus the Hop Shop was born.

William and Caroline were often asked by their hop customers if they sold any other dried flowers. At that time Dutch wholesalers commanded some 90 per cent of the market in the UK, where production was generally small-scale and lacking in quality.

The opportunity was therefore identified to start drying bunches of cereals and grasses, crops whose production requirements were already familiar. It soon became very evident that to compete effectively with the quality and range of imports, further studies would be essential. They entered an award scheme—Venturecash sponsored by National Westminster Bank, National Farmers Union and National Young Farmers Club—which was designed to assist young agriculturalists to research promising diversification projects. They won one of the £1,000 awards which enabled them to broaden the research on growing, drying and marketing flowers. A visit was made to Holland to see their fresh and dried flower markets, seed merchants, as well as wholesale and retail companies.

Discussions were arranged with interested potential customers to learn more about the various quality criteria they sought when purchasing dried flowers. Advice was gathered from specialists on growing outdoor flowers on a field scale, kiln design for drying and retailing techniques. All the information gathered was used to plan the financial investment into the new enterprise. Previously redundant farm buildings were selected for the construction of special high-temperature drying kilns, into which trolleys (made and welded by me) with flower bunches on them would be wheeled. Other buildings were required for controlled-atmosphere storage and for a suitably sited farm shop. The problems were many, but solutions had to be discovered quickly to ensure a high-quality, well-packaged product, with a competitive price tag.

William manages the growing of the many annual and perennial flowers which add a colourful view growing alongside more traditional crops. Hand cutting, bunching and kiln drying now occupies most fine days between May and September. Drying times depend upon flower type and can vary from as little as 24 hours to two weeks, after which they are boxed, ready for storage or despatch. Scrupulous quality control at every stage is essential to achieve best results, and this careful attention to detail has been responsible for developing a good reputation among an increasing number of customers.

Caroline has developed the marketing side of the venture, with the flowers being

The Hop Shop.

Flowers being harvested.

supplied to wholesalers, florists and other customers as well as from the shop at Castle Farm. Recent successes have included export orders to Sweden, and to the USA for use at a Celebrity Gala Evening.

William and Caroline were founder members of the British Dried Flowers Association, formed in 1988. In April 1991, Caroline co-authored a book entitled *Dried Flower Gardening*. Her father, Douglas Keen, created Ladybird Books and it had been her ambition to publish a book of her own. This book gives inspiration for anyone interested in the growing and the drying of flowers from their own garden.

Norfolk Royal apples.

Office Bookkeeping progress

The necessity to keep farm data and records had become more and more time-consuming every year albeit with the help of sophisticated office equipment.

The simple office needs that our mother used for many years comprised a pen with a bottle of ink, a pencil, a rubber and a ruler. The introduction of carbon paper was quite an advancement and the appearance of biro pens was a marvel as they gave much clearer carbon copies.

We have always kept good basic records about livestock and field crops. The first entries for crop records are written on special postcard-sized cards, printed in three different colours and rulings. They are for fertilizer applications, seed sowing and spraying information, which is duly entered into the field record book in the office. Crop yields, date of harvest, soil analysis and other useful details are also written in the book.

We employed our first farm secretary, Jean Mayoss, in 1974 when Gran Alexander retired after fifty-five years of devoted office record-keeping and letter writing. The first major purchase of office equipment then appeared in the purchase ledger: a typewriter. James and I found it a real luxury to dictate a letter and then just have to sign it. In January 1980 when Mrs Mayoss left the district we engaged Pauline Holden. Her impeccable book-keeping, cheerful disposition and keenness to keep everything up to date has been of immeasurable help to the smooth running of the farming business from the separate offices of Home Farm and Castle Farm.

In order to keep abreast with the office needs, our latest purchases have included a photocopier, computer, fax machine and radio communications to buildings and tractors. The first use for which we bought a computer was to work out employees' wages. The necessary calculations had become more time-consuming with the advent of PAYE, NIC, holiday pay, sickness pay, maternity allowance and end-of-year tax and insurance reconciliation details. What a boon it has been that our sons were born in time to absorb these ever-increasing statutory requirements and regulations.

The livestock records for several hundred animals are so much more easily kept on a computer, which is able to extract varying lists of details at the press of a key. A computer with a print-out has been an essential office requirement for the Hop Shop business. Besides storing and providing customer information, the computer prints self-adhesive labels for the stock of filled boxes of sixty or more types of dried flowers and also the address labels when flowers are despatched.

Business budgets and cash flows are two other functions in which a computer excels. But we must never forget there's no output without input and that rubbish in gives rubbish out. The boys and Pauline say it is quite easy to operate when you know how; however James and I have not strayed into the computer world—we are very happy just to watch other operators.

Machinery Purchase decisions

There have been tremendous technological advancements and improvements in all forms of farm equipment used on the land as well as in buildings, particularly during the last two decades. Mechanical feeding of livestock, movement of grain and mechanized hop-picking are some examples within our farming enterprises. The decision of when to purchase new field machinery has always been an ongoing consideration. The right decision will perhaps never have been more critical during our lifetime than during these next few years.

Up until about the mid-1970s, farmers were being urged to increase their production of a wide range of products. Government grant aid was given for approved farm development schemes which were considered financially sound. The result was an increase in the number of four-wheel drive and higher horse-power tractors, and, complementary to them, were wider and more sophisticated cultivation and harvesting equipment. The benefits of this upgrading were a reduction in the number of man-hours per acre and the improvement in the timing of operations related to weather conditions. A practical example being that instead of a tractor pulling a three-furrow reversible plough, we now use a five-furrow one with a vari-width feature. This allows on-the-move adjustment of furrow widths from twelve inches to twenty inches. On our steep fields the tractor is always capable of ploughing a wider width downhill than uphill. Many of the cultivation implements have hydraulic folding wings, which doubles their effective width. Tractor driver comfort has received a lot of attention and the driver now enjoys an air-conditioned safety cab equipped with a radio. There is a formidable number of levers, knobs and buttons to use in conjunction with in-cab electronic equipment displaying such information as speed of travel, acres worked, volume of spray used and many other related details. Combine harvesters can be equipped with read-outs giving weights of grain harvested as well as the yield per acre.

Agricultural Training Boards have been established all over the country offering a broad spectrum of courses at which both employers and employees attend lectures and practical demonstrations on any subject relating to agriculture and horticulture. These courses have proved to be extremely successful. Training is virtually an integral necessity for all persons working on farms.

Looking to the future

In this last decade of the century, farming is being run down at a faster rate than any of us wish to see. There is no doubt, that many farming businesses will not remain viable. Increasing production is a challenge which farmers have always been able to meet but going into reverse creates extremely difficult situations.

Environmental issues are a dominant subject in today's discussions. New regulations are coming into force almost faster than we are able to adapt to them. A total ban on straw burning will become law after the 1992 harvest. Straw choppers and chaff spreaders will probably be standard equipment on combine harvesters. We are already finding them very helpful when incorporating straw.

Another regulation which particularly concerns those farmers with livestock and especially those who have land near waterways is the disposal of farm effluent. Also the excessive use of nitrogenous fertilizers in certain locations is subject to government legislation.

The years 1989 and 1990 had very hot summers with little rain and most crops suffered drought conditions. The river Darent was once a flourishing trout stream. It is fed from the waterlogged chalk that floors its valley, rather than surface run-off water. Today the river bed in many sections often dries up in the summer, partially because of the droughts but mainly due to the chain of bore hole pumping stations. They supply an increasing volume of water to an increasing number of houses and factories within the Greater London area. This over-abstraction is drying out the lovely water meadows that our grandparents treasured so much. Who knows how much longer will there be a river Darent? This environmental problem is certainly not of the farmers' making.

The crystal ball shows a very hazy picture of the future. But in spite of all the problems that may arise, I am sure that the Alexander generations will continue to farm in the Darent valley. I sincerely hope that in the future when they visit the hilly countryside around Lochwinnoch, they will appreciate the courageous decision which James and Jane Alexander took in moving with their young family from East Auchengown in Renfrewshire to Home Farm, Eynsford, on the fourth of February 1892.

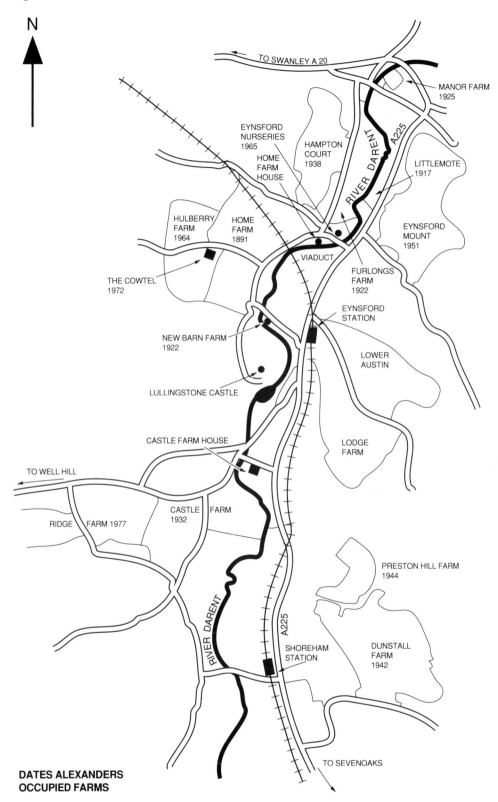

N

DATES ALEXANDERS
OCCUPIED FARMS

APPENDIX I
Cropping Details

22.4.91

HOME FARM
Rented 1891 – Bought 1952

Young stock, grazing, cereals, oil seed rape, peas, maize, grass seed.

LITTLE MOTE
Bought 1917

Garage building and grazing.

FURLONGS FARM
Bought 1922

Grain store, livestock housing, grazing for dairy replacements.

NEW BARN FARM
Rented 1922 – Bought 1973 – Sold 1977

(Dairying) SOLD

MANOR FARM
Rented 1925 – Bought 1933

Cereals and grazing.

CASTLE FARM
Rented 1932 – Bought 1948

Hops, apples, dried flowers, cereals, oil seed rape, maize, grass seed, grain store and live-stock housing.

HAMPTON COURT land
Rented 1938 – Bought 1952

Cereals and oil seed rape.

DUNSTALL FARM
Rented 1942

Rearing calves and young stock, grazing, cereals, oil seed rape and maize.

PRESTON HILL land
Rented 1944

Cereals.

EYNSFORD MOUNT land
Bought 1951

Cereals, oil seed rape and grass seed.

HULBERRY FARM
Bought 1964

Dairy herd, grazing, maize and cereals.

EYNSFORD NURSERIES
Bought 1965 – Sold 1976

(Flowers) SOLD.

LOWER AUSTIN LODGE FARM
Rented 1971 – Bought 1985

Grain store, cereals, oil seed rape and dried flowers.

RIDGE FARM
Bought 1977

Cereals, oil seed rape and grass seed.

CROPPING ACREAGES

Wheat	599	Grazing	265	
Barley	476	Hops	37	
Oil Seed Rape	196	Apples	7	
Peas	22	Dried Flowers	27	
Maize	96	Woodland	88	
Grass Seed	78	Roads, Buildings, etc.	79	

LIVESTOCK

Dairy Cows	135
Young Stock	91
Beef	194
	420

Total 1970 Acres

APPENDIX II

AGRICULTURAL WAGES RATES 1919–1991

DATE OF WAGE CHANGE (a)	MINIMUM RATE	SUMMER HOURS (b)	WINTER HOURS	PAID HOLIDAYS	BANK HOLIDAYS (c)	COTTAGE RENT PER WEEK
6.10.19	£1 19s. 6d.	50	48			
27. 2.22	£1 11s. 6d.	54	48			
9.10.22	£1 7s. 0d.	50	48			
2. 3.26	£1 12s. 6d.	52	48			3s 0d
2. 4.39	£1 15s. 0d.	52	48	3 days	ABC	3s 0d
20. 6.43	£3 0s. 0d.	52	48	4 days	ABCD	3s 0d
4. 3.45	£3 10s. 0d.	52	48	6 days	ABCDEF	3s 0d
7. 4.46	£3 10s. 0d.	48	6 days		ABCDEF	3s 0d
13. 3.49	£4 14s. 0d.	47	7 days		ABCDEF	6s 0d
21.10.51	£5 8s. 0d.	47	12 days		ABCDEF	6s 0d
22. 2.60	£8 0s. 0d.	46	12 days		ABCDEF	6s 0d
18.11.63	£9 10s. 0d.	45	12 days		ABCDEF	6s 0d
4. 1.65	£10 2s. 0d.	45	12 days		ABCDEF	6s 0d
3. 1.66	£10 10s. 0d.	44	12 days		ABCDEF	6s 0d
2. 2.70	£13 3s. 0d.	43	12 days		ABCDEF	6s 0d
15. 2.71	£14.80	42	12 days		ABCDEF	6s 0d
17. 1.72	£16.20	42	3 weeks		ABCDEF	50p
22. 1.73	£19.50	42	3 weeks		ABCDEF	50p
22. 1.74	£21.80	40	3 weeks		ABCDEFG	50p
20. 1.76	£36.50	40	3 weeks		ABCDEFG	£1.50
20. 1.78	£43.00	40	3 weeks		ABCDEFGH	£1.50
20. 1.80	£58.00	40	3 weeks + 2 days		ABCDEFGH	£1.50
21. 1.81	£64.00	40	3 weeks + 4 days		ABCDEFGH	£1.50
21. 1.82	£70.40	40	4 weeks		ABCDEFGH	£1.50
5. 6.88	£104.20	40	4 weeks		ABCDEFGH	£1.50
4. 6.89	£112.02	40	4 weeks		ABCDEFGH	£1.50
3. 6.90	£122.10	40	4 weeks		ABCDEFGH	£1.50
2. 6.91	£129.43	39	4 weeks + 1 day		ABCDEFGH	£1.50

(a)   New wage rates are omitted between the dates listed when there are no changes in the other columns.

(b)   Summer Hours 1st MARCH–31st OCTOBER until 1st NOVEMBER 1945

(c)   A.   EASTER MONDAY   E.   GOOD FRIDAY
      B.   CHRISTMAS DAY   F.   AUGUST BANK HOLIDAY MONDAY
      C.   BOXING DAY   G.   NEW YEAR's DAY
      D.   WHIT MONDAY   H.   MAY DAY (first Monday)

APPENDIX III
1919 Wage Card

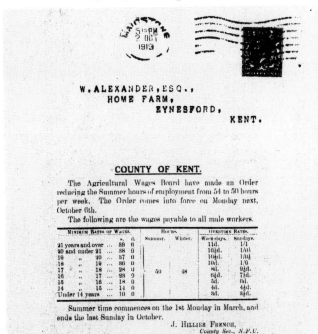

The daily diary for Christmas week 1918 of Stephen Friend age 41 who worked at Home Farm.

APPENDIX IV
"The Priory" Eynsford

24.12.1763

THIS INDENTURE made in the twenty fourth day of December in the fourth year of the Reign of our Sovereign Lord George the third day by the Grace of God of Great Britain France and Ireland King Defender of the faith and in the year of our Lord one thousand seven hundred and sixty three BETWEEN Richard Mandy of Eynsford in the County of Kent husbandman and Katherine his wife of the one part and Thomas Bellsham of Fawkham in the said county of Kent carpenter of the other part. WITNESSETH that for and in consideration of the sum of one hundred and fifty five pounds of lawful money of Great Britain to the said Richard Mandy in hand well and truly paid by the said Thomas Bellsham at and before the sealing and delivery of these presents The Receipt whereof and himself to be thenceforth fully paid and satisfied to the said Richard Mandy doth hereby vouchsafe and acknowledge and thereof and therefrom and of and from every part thereof doth acquit release and discharge the said Thomas Bellsham his Heirs Executors and Administrators and every of them for ever by these presents to the said Richard Mandy HATH allowed granted bargained sold demised released and confirmed and by these presents DOTH allow grant bargain sell demise release and confirm unto the said Thomas Bellsham in his actual possession and seisin now being by force and virtue of a Bargain and Sale to him thereof made by the said Richard Mandy for the consideration of five shillings by Indenture bearing date the day next before the Day of the Date of these presents for the term of one whole year commencing from the Day next before the Day of the Date of the same Indenture of Bargain and Sale and by force of the Statute made for transferring of Uses into possession and to his heirs and assigns.

N.B. This is about one quarter of the length of the document

APPENDIX V

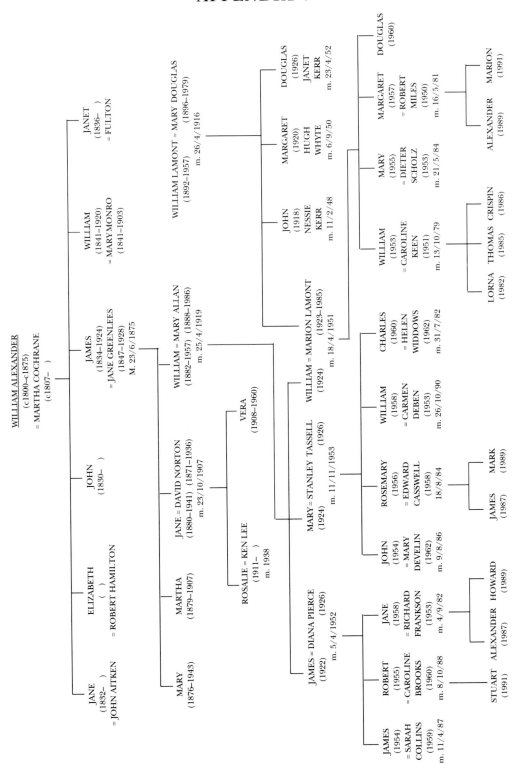

APPENDIX VI

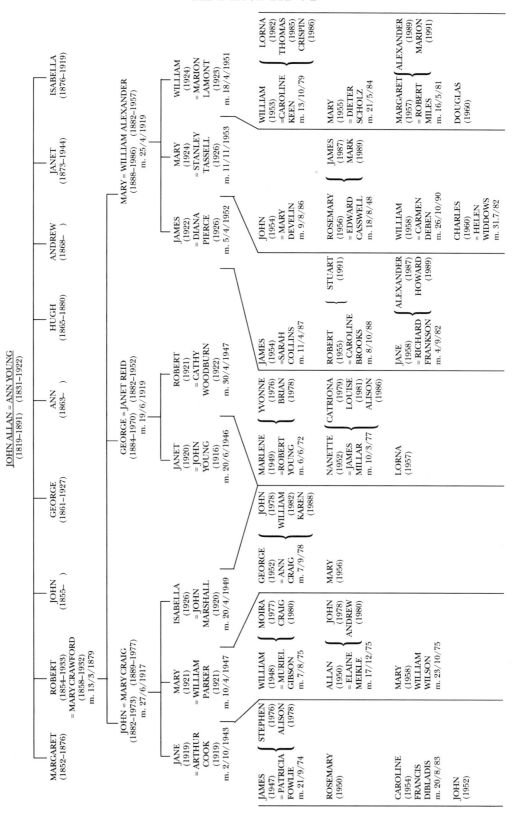

APPENDIX VII

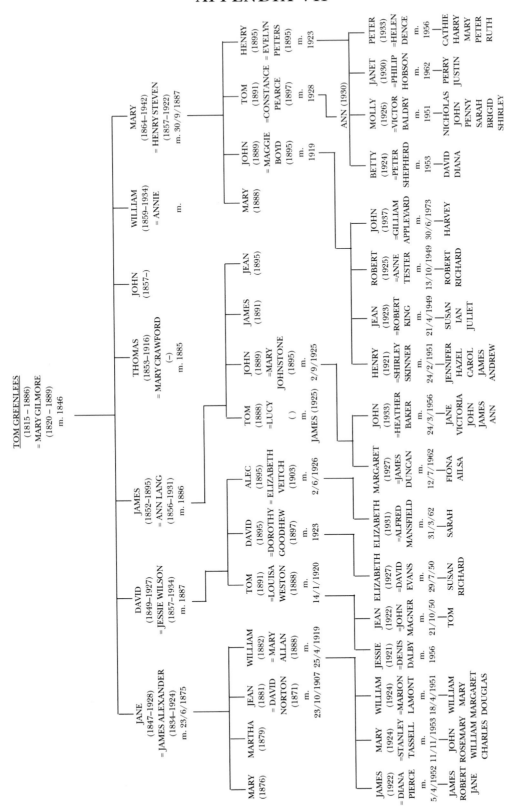

APPENDIX VIII

William and Diana Alexander.

William and Caroline Alexander and family.

Douglas Alexander.

Dieter and Mary Scholz.

Robert and Margaret Miles and family.

James and Diana Alexander.

James and Sarah Alexander.

1991 FAMILY PHOTOGRAPHS

Stanley and Mary Tassell.

John and Mary Tassell.

Edward and Rosemary Casswell and family.

William and Carmen Tassell.

Charles and Helen Tassell.

Robert, Caroline and Stuart Alexander.

Richard and Jane Frankson and family.

APPENDIX IX
Alexander Sayings

I wish I could have my second thoughts first.

―――――――――

The curse of lending is getting things back.

―――――――――

It takes less time to put things away
than it does to look for them.

―――――――――

I am allowed to do one silly thing each year.

―――――――――

It is not so much what you do
but how you do it that matters most.

―――――――――

Farm as if you're going to live for ever.
Live as if you're going to die tomorrow.

―――――――――

Problems are sent to make you think not to make you worry.
It is thinking of the solution that is the problem.

―――――――――

As the boys grow older they need more expensive toys.

―――――――――

Always try and make your head save your heels.

―――――――――

You can never do too much in dry weather.

―――――――――

Index

Note: page references to illustrations are in italics.